The Crab and its Relatives

by the same author

VANISHING ANIMALS

The marbled swimming crab, *Portunus depurator*. The large eyes can be seen sunk in pits along the front edge of the carapace. The fourth pair of legs, with their flattened terminal segments modified for swimming, are carried above the level of the other legs

The Crab
and its Relatives

PHILIP STREET

FABER AND FABER LIMITED

24 Russell Square London

First published in mcmlxvi
by Faber and Faber Limited
24 Russell Square London W.C.1
Printed in Great Britain by
Latimer Trend & Co Ltd Plymouth

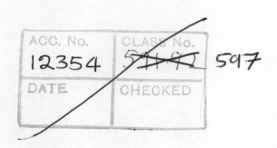
© *Philip Street* 1966

Contents

Contents

Illustrations

7

Illustrations

Illustrations

9

Illustrations

Preface

Despite the large number of books published on various aspects of British natural history in the last few decades, for certain groups there is still no book available for the amateur naturalist and those interested in animal life. This book aims to fill one of those gaps, for it is a very long time since a general survey of the natural history of the British Crustacea was attempted. As far as possible I have adopted the biographical approach, believing that most people are more interested in how an animal lives its life than in the details of its structure. I have thus included only as much of the anatomy of the Crustacea as is necessary to understand their natural history.

All the photographs illustrating the book are my own, but for the excellent drawings, which add so much to it, I am indebted to my friend Megan Di Girolamo. The task of compiling the index has once again been undertaken by my friend Mary Thomson.

1 · *Introducing the Crustacea*

The crab belongs to the vast assemblage of animals known as arthropods, or jointed-limbed animals. Whether judged by the number of their species, the total number of individuals, or by the extent of their geographical distribution the arthropods cannot be challenged as the most successful of all groups of animals, the vertebrates not excepted. The group consists of the insects, which themselves contain more than three-quarters of all known animal species, the spiders and scorpions, the centipedes and millipedes, and the crustaceans, comprising the crab and its numerous relatives, which include the shrimps, lobsters, prawns, water fleas, barnacles and woodlice.

The Crustacea are in a sense complementary to the insects and the other groups, for whereas these are predominantly terrestrial, with only a tiny minority of species adapted for life in water, the Crustacea are almost exclusively aquatic, having only a few representatives rather inadequately adapted to live on land. In the seas they are almost as abundant and widespread as the insects are on land.

Although this book is primarily concerned with the natural history of the Crustacea and not with the details of their anatomy, in order to understand how they live, and how they are adapted to their chosen modes of life, some knowledge of their structure is necessary. In common with all the arthropods the crustaceans have a segmented body. In the ancestral Crustacea each segment probably had its pair of functional appendages, but in most living forms, a variable number of segments have either lost their appendages altogether, or have retained only rudiments of them.

The whole surface of the body is enclosed in an external skeleton consisting of a layer of chitin covered on the outside with a thin layer of waxy substance. Chitin itself is a horny flexible material, but over much of the body it is strengthened with a variety of other substances which also make it rigid. Between consecutive segments, except in the head region, the chitin usually remains unstrengthened, as it does between the joints of the limbs, thus giving flexibility to both the trunk and the limbs. The body as a whole consists of the head, containing the first six segments and their appendages, and the trunk, representing a variable number of segments.

In the head the chitin between the segments is also strengthened, so that the whole head is covered with a rigid skeleton. In some species the skeletons of varying numbers of thoracic segments are similarly fused together to give added protection. In many species, too, a fold of chitin begins at the back of the head and extends backwards over some of the trunk segments as a protective shield over the back. It may also bend downwards so as to cover in the sides as well, and may in addition become fused with the dorsal parts of the thoracic skeleton. This fold is called the carapace, and is often very considerably strengthened. In the crabs and lobsters, together with the head skeleton with which it is of course continuous, it forms the hard shell.

While an external skeleton has many advantages, it has

one great disadvantage. Once it has been laid down, it becomes impossible for the animal within to grow in size. It is thus necessary for it to be shed periodically and be replaced by a slightly larger one. This moulting or ecdysis is brought about by enzymes which dissolve away the inner layers of chitin. This enables the occupant to split the old skeleton and slide out of it. While the body is increasing in size and the new skeleton is being formed the larger crustacea go into hiding, because without the protection of a skeleton they are extremely vulnerable to their enemies. Before ecdysis is due to begin a crustacean lays down a considerable store of food within its body. This enables it to grow rapidly during the short time it takes for the new skeleton to be laid down and hardened.

Between them the appendages have to cater for a great variety of functions, but those of any particular segment tend to concentrate on just one or perhaps two of these. Appendages are responsible for locomotion, both swimming and walking, and obtaining food. This may involve catching large prey and dismembering it, or filtering out minute particles suspended in the water or stirred up from the bottom by the action of other appendages. The conveyance of food to the mouth, and breaking it up into smaller pieces if necessary, is also a job for special appendages. Others again act as gills, and are responsible for extracting sufficient oxygen from the water, often from a special respiratory current set up by the activities of these or other appendages. Modified appendages in some species act as copulatory organs, and females use others for attaching the fertilized eggs while they hatch. Appendages, too, behave as sense organs, especially for the sense of touch, chemical senses (taste and smell), and the sense of balance.

Only in the head region is there any uniformity throughout the group in the functions carried out by the appendages of a particular segment. In the developing embryo the head is seen to be derived from the first six segments, with an additional contribution from a presegmental region in front of the first segment. The first segment, however, almost completely disappears as development proceeds, but the other five are all represented in the adult, and each has a pair of appendages. The second segment gives rise to a pair of antennules and the third to a pair of antennae, the function of both pairs being sensory. The appendages of the last three head segments are all mouth parts, between them being responsible for manipulating the food and passing it into the mouth. The pair on the fourth segment are called mandibles, on the fifth the maxillules (or first maxillae), and on the sixth the maxillae (or second maxillae). In many of the higher Crustacea the first two or three pairs of thoracic appendages form additional mouth parts known as maxillipeds. The functions of the remaining thoracic and the abdominal appendages can only be considered in the individual groups, because of the great diversity of function which we have already noted.

Although so diverse in function and appearance, all these crustacean appendages conform to a basic biramous or two-branched type. Fundamentally each consists of a basic portion, the protopodite, with two branches attached at its free end. The outer branch is known as the exopodite and the inner one the endopodite. The protopodite may consist of a single piece, or contain as many as four jointed portions. The branches may also each consist of a number of jointed sections. In addition the basal portion may have one or more additional processes attached along its outer edge. These are known as epipodites, and may be modified as gills. The typical slender much-jointed limb is known as a stenopo-

 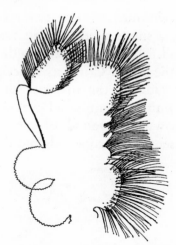

Fig. 1. A typical stenopodium   Fig. 2. A typical phyllopodium

dium. Some species possess a number of broad flat lobed limbs with very thin cuticles, the shape of the limb being maintained by the pressure of blood within it and not by the strength of the cuticle. Because of its thin cuticle the phyllopodium, as this limb is called, does not need to be provided with joints, but the various lobes can be seen to represent the various parts present in the stenopodium. In addition to epipodites along the outer edge of the basic portion, these phyllopodia also bear lobes along the inner edge. These are called endites, and are seldom found on stenopodia. The only appendage which does not conform to the biramous type is the antennule. This has only a single shaft in most species, though in some of the higher Crustacea it develops a second branch. These branches, however, are not thought to represent the original endopodite and exopodite.

The Crustacea are well supplied with sense organs. The nauplius larva, which as we shall see occurs during the development of at least some of the members of every group, has a single median eye situated towards the front of the head. This eye persists into the adult in most species, though in the higher Crustacea it becomes vestigial and functionless. In addition the majority of Crustacea develop a pair of prominent compound eyes similar in structure to the well-known compound eyes of insects. These, however, are absent in the copepods and the adult cirripedes.

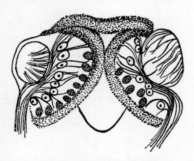

Fig. 3. The crustacean median eye

Fig. 4. One of the ommatidia or units which form the crustacean compound eye

The median eye consists of three pigmented cups, one central and the others on either side of it. The cups are lined with retinal cells which are sensitive to light, each cell continuing as a nerve fibre to the brain. In some species each cup also has a transparent lens to concentrate the light on to the retinal cells. In some of the copepods the two lateral cups have migrated to the sides of the head, thus occupying a similar position to the compound eyes of the other groups.

A compound eye consists of a large number of long thin tapering bodies packed tightly together. Each one is surrounded by pigmented cells to prevent light passing through to or from its neighbours. At its outer wider end the cuticle is modified to form a convex lens, beneath which is a crystalline cone whose function is to concentrate the light on to a bundle of long thin light-sensitive retinal cells. At the base of the body these cells continue as nerve fibres to the brain. Because of their tapering shape and the way they are packed each body faces in a slightly different direction from its neighbours, so that the whole eye gives an extremely wide angle of vision. The compound eye in fact is admirably designed to detect movement from almost any quarter, rather than to give clear images.

The bristles which are so abundant on many Crustacea are not useless ornaments. Many of them are sensory in function. These are hollow walls of chitin filled with extensions from the epidermis, which lies immediately beneath the cuticle and is in fact responsible for secreting it after each moult. Nerve fibrils are also present, and are stimulated whenever the bristle is moved, so that it functions as a tactile or touch sense organ. In addition to these touch sense bristles there are others with similar structure but with much thinner chitinous walls. These act as chemical sense organs, being able to detect the presence of various substances in the surrounding water. They are thus the organs of smell and taste, and are particularly abundant on the antennules. They may be present as well on the antennae, but these tend to have mainly tactile bristles.

The higher Crustacea have a special organ of balance called a statocyst. It consists of a hollow pit, situated usually at the base of an antennule, and opening to the exterior by means of a tiny pore, so that it is filled with the water in which the animal is living. The floor of the pit is lined with tactile bristles supplied with nerve fibres. Resting on these bristles are sand grains which the animal picked up and deposited there at its last moult. Any rolling or pitching movements which the animal makes result in the sand grains rolling on to different bristles, and their consequent nerve messages to the brain enable the creature to know at all times how it is orientated, and thus to take the necessary steps to right itself.

The final proof that the statocyst really did act in this way was obtained by taking a shrimp which had just moulted and putting it into clean water with some iron filings as the only available particles. The shrimp duly picked up the filings and placed a few of them in each of the two pits. The investigator then held a powerful electro-magnet above the water. Immediately the shrimp turned right over on its back and continued to swim upside down so long as the magnet was switched on. Only in this position would the filings be pressing against the bristles on which the sand grains would normally be resting when the creature was swimming the right way up! Thus as far as it was able to tell from the evidence coming from its statocysts it was in fact swimming the right way up.

The crustacea go a long way back into evolutionary history. The earliest known fossil arthropods are the trilobites, some of which are found in rocks estimated to be at least 400 million years old. They apparently died out nearly 200 million years ago. Their interest to us is that in general structure they resemble the Crustacea, which are indeed believed to have been evolved from them. The Trilobite body was wide and flattened, in

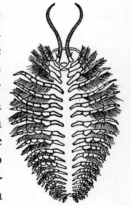

Fig. 5. A fossil trilobite

Introducing the Crustacea

general appearance something like that of a modern wood-louse. Like the woodlouse, too, it could roll itself up into a ball, presumably for protection. All along the trunk were numerous pairs of biramous limbs, their endopodites being clearly jointed and leg-like, while their thinner exopodites carried a fringe of bristles. The first-stage trilobite larvae consisted of just three head segments, like the modern first nauplius larva. As development proceeded more and more segments were added on behind.

The following outline classification of the Crustacea should help the reader to find his way around the rest of the book. Species mentioned are those dealt with as principal representatives in the subsequent chapters.

Phylum ARTHROPODA
Sub-phylum CRUSTACEA

Class 1.   BRANCHIOPODA. The majority of the branchio-pods are fresh-water forms. Only *Artemia* (the brine shrimp) and a few other marine forms live in salt water. Important members are *Chirocephalus* (the fairy shrimp), *Apus*, and *Daphnia* and its relatives (the water fleas).

Class 2.   OSTRACODA. A small group of tiny crustaceans whose carapace has developed into a bivalve shell completely enclosing the body. *Cypris* is a common British fresh-water creature, and *Cypridina* an important marine representative.

Class 3.   COPEPODA. The copepods are an extremely important group, since their representatives form the majority of the crustacea found in the plankton both in the seas and in fresh water. *Calanus* is the most important marine copepod, and *Cyclops* the most important in fresh water. The class also contains a number of common fish parasites, for example *Chondracanthus*, *Caligus* and *Lernaea*.

Class 4. BRANCHIURA. A small group of temporary parasites known as carp-lice, which are strong swimmers but attach themselves to the gills of fishes, both marine and fresh water. They feed on blood drawn from the gill filaments by a suctorial mouth. *Argulus*. The Branchiura used to be included with the Copepoda.

Class 5. CIRRIPEDIA. These are the most modified of all the Crustacea, the adults of most species bearing no apparent resemblance to Crustacea at all. Their true affinities, however, are revealed by their development through normal crustacean larvae. They are all sedentary creatures in the adult stage, and the majority of them are hermaphrodite. The common ship or goose barnacle (*Lepas*), the acorn barnacles (*Balanus*, etc.) of the seashore rocks, and the parasitic sac barnacle (*Sacculina*) which parasitizes crabs, are the important members of the group.

Class 6. MALACOSTRACA. These are the higher Crustacea, the true shrimps, many other shrimp-like creatures, the prawns, the lobsters, the crabs, the woodlice, etc. There are five sub-classes and numerous orders. Consideration of the Malacostraca will occupy a considerable portion of the book.

Sub-class LEPTOSTRACA. *Nebalia*—common species of rock pools.

Sub-class HOPLOCARIDA (STOMATOPODA). Marine burrowing crustacea. *Squilla mantis*, the mantis shrimp.

Introducing the Crustacea

Sub-class SYNCARIDA. Fresh water. *Bathynella* from subterranean waters in Europe.

Sub-class PERICARIDA. A large and important sub-class containing five orders.

Order MYSIDACEA. Opossum shrimps, so-called because they carry their young in a brood pouch. *Mysis*.

Order CUMACEA. Small marine crustacea which live in mud or sand. *Diastylis*.

Order TANAIDACEA. Small Crustacea which usually live in burrows or tubes. *Apseudes* and *Tanais*.

Order ISOPODA. Shore slaters (*Ligia*), woodlice (*Armadillidium*), hog-slater (*Asellus*) and various parasitic forms, all with flattened bodies. Also includes the notorious marine wood-borer, the gribble (*Limnoria*).

Order AMPHIPODA. Body flattened from side to side. Fresh-water shrimps (*Gammarus*), sand or shore hoppers (*Orchestria, Talitrus*), skeleton shrimp (*Caprella*).

Sub-class EUCARIDA. A large sub-class containing all the higher Crustacea—shrimps, prawns, crayfishes, crawfishes, lobsters and crabs.

Order EUPHAUSIACEA. An important group of planktonic marine shrimp-like creatures, some of which form the food of the whalebone whales—they are the krill of the Norwegian whalers. Also distinguished by their phosphorescent spots. *Euphausia, Meganyctiphanes, Nyctiphanes*.

Order DECAPODA. This order contains all the other members of the sub-class.

Sub-order PENAEIDEA. Primitive prawns. *Leucifer, Penaeus*.

Sub-order CARIDEA. Prawns and shrimps proper. *Leander, Crangon*.

Introducing the Crustacea

Sub-order ASTACURA. Crayfishes and lobsters. *Astacus, Homarus, Nephrops.*

Sub-order PALINURA. Crawfishes. *Palinurus.*

Sub-order ANOMURA. Hermit crabs (*Eupagurus*), robber crabs (*Birgus*), stone crabs (*Lithodes*), squat lobsters (*Galathea*), porcelain crabs (*Porcellana*).

Sub-order BRACHYURA. True crabs. Edible crab (*Cancer*), shore crab (*Carcinus*), spider crabs (*Maia*, etc.), true land crabs (*Gecarcinus*).

2 · Fairy Shrimps and Water Fleas— the Branchiopods and the Ostracods

Such evidence as we have suggests that the ancestral crustacean had a trunk consisting of a considerable number of segments each having a pair of appendages all built on the same pattern. Every appendage carried out a variety of functions, swimming, catching food and breathing, as well as acting as a sense organ. No carapace had developed to cover any of the trunk segments. Only in the head was there any differentiation of structure and function between the appendages. If this is so, then the most primitive living crustacean is the little fresh-water fairy shrimp, *Chirocephalus diaphanus*.

Fig. 6. The fairy shrimp, *Chirocephalus diaphanus*

Its head is a typical modern crustacean head, with a median eye and a pair of stalked lateral eyes, unbranched

antennules and branched antennae, followed by paired mandibles, maxillules and maxillae. The first eleven segments of
the trunk, however, carry pairs of phyllopodia which are
all alike in structure and size. They are incessantly on the
move, propelling the tiny restless creature through the
water, and setting up a feeding and breathing current. This
current is drawn in at the front of the trunk and flows backwards along the median groove between the right and left
rows of appendages. As it passes down this groove a portion
of it flows out through the gaps between succeeding appendages. On the endites forming the inner edge of each
appendage there is a veritable hedge of bristles which are
directed backwards almost at right-angles to the plane of
the appendage. The water which passes out through the
gaps thus has to pass through these bristles, which trap
minute algae and other organisms contained in the water.
These are gathered up by a subsidiary current of water right
at the top of the median groove. This travels in the reverse
direction to the main current below it, and so carries the
trapped food forward to the head, where the appendages
guide it into the mouth. Beyond the endite bristles the water
passes over the thin-walled epipodite which serves as a gill.

After the eleven thoracic segments with their paired
appendages there is another segment which is regarded as
the twelfth thoracic. It lacks phyllopodia, but does have a
pair of protrusible penes in the male by which the spermatozoa are transferred to the female. In the female the corresponding parts of this pair of segments are developed into a
single median egg pouch. These penes and egg pouch are
regarded as a much modified twelfth pair of thoracic appendages. In the male, too, the antennae are developed and
modified into a 'frontal organ' which is used by the male to
grasp the female during mating. The seven abdominal seg-

ments are without trace of appendages, and the telson bears a pair of narrow pointed caudal rami fringed with hairs and forming a forked tail.

In its habits the fairy shrimp is an interesting creature. It is about half an inch long, transparent and almost colourless except for its black eyes and the reddened tips of its appendages, and always swims upside down on its back. Although it is exclusively a fresh-water creature, you will never find it in a pond or any other permanent stretch of water. It lives only in temporary pools of water which appear in the rainy season and dry up during the summer months. Wherever there is a habitat, however unlikely it may seem for the support of life, there is certain to be animals adapted to live there. And the fairy shrimp is one of the most successful of those aquatic organisms adapted to life in temporary pools.

While there is water in the pool in which it lives the fairy shrimp feeds on microscopic algae and other organisms, themselves adapted to the same intermittent life. After mating, its eggs are not shed, but are stored in the special egg pouch. When the pool begins to dry up all the fairy shrimps die, and their bodies sink into the mud. The eggs in their pouches, however, remain alive but dormant, a state in which they are able to exist indefinitely. The following year, when the pool again appears, the eggs finally develop and ensure that once again the pool has its population of fairy shrimps. Sometimes fairy shrimps appear in a temporary pool which has not had them before. In such cases it is most likely that brood pouches have been carried from their original dried-up pools in mud adhering to birds' feet. Fairy shrimps are widespread in many part of the world. In Iraq, for example, they are the most common organisms in temporary pools which occur everywhere during the rainy season.

Fairy Shrimps and Water Fleas—

There is good reason to believe that the fairy shrimps are so well adapted physiologically to temporary pool life that their eggs will not in fact develop until they have undergone a period of desiccation. This would explain their absence from permanent stretches of water, for here they could not reproduce because their eggs would be incapable of developing.

The class Branchiopoda, to which the fairy shrimp belongs, contains the most primitive living crustacea. They are almost all fresh-water creatures, the most important exception being the brine shrimp, *Artemia salina*, which goes to the opposite extreme, and can only exist in salt lakes and salt pans where the salt concentration is much above that of normal sea water. In appearance it is very similar to the fairy shrimp, and is indeed closely related to it.

The fairy and brine shrimps belong to the order Anostraca, one of the three orders into which the members of the class are divided. The second order, the Notostraca, is a

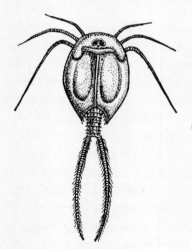

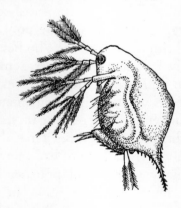

Fig. 8. The water flea, *Daphnia*

Fig. 7. *Apus cancriformis*

small one containing only one comparatively rare British representative, *Apus cancriformis*, which in fact is of almost world-wide distribution. Its appearance is very distinctive. Much of the trunk is covered with a broad shield-shaped carapace, the last segments projecting beyond this and ending in two long curved caudal rami. There are eleven thoracic segments each bearing a pair of phyllopodia. These are followed by twenty-two abdominal segments. The first two of these carry a pair of phyllopodia, the next fifteen between two and five pairs each, while the last five segments are devoid of appendages. From front to back the appendages decrease progressively in size. The multiplication of the appendages on the abdominal segments is probably another indication of the primitive nature of the Branchiopoda, for it corresponds to the similar multiplication seen in the fossil trilobites.

The majority of the Branchiopoda belong to the third order, the Diplostraca. Two sub-orders are recognized, the Conchostraca, which has no British representatives, and the Cladocera, which includes the water fleas. The best known of these water fleas are *Daphnia* and *Simocephalus*, which are present and often incredibly abundant in a large proportion of our lakes, ponds and ditches. Their principal structural features are a pair of very prominent and relatively large antennae, and a large carapace, which extends right down the sides of the body beyond the tips of the appendages, and backwards beyond the last trunk segment, so that the whole of the body is completely enclosed in a shell flattened from side to side. The two compound eyes have migrated to the centre of the head, where they have fused to a single prominent median compound eye which is characteristic of the group.

Compared with the other Branchiopoda the body of the

29

cladocerans has been greatly shortened by the loss of segments. There are only five thoracic segments, each bearing a pair of appendages, and three pairs of abdominal segments which are without appendages. Since they are completely enclosed within the carapace, the thoracic limbs cannot be used for locomotion. Instead the little creatures swim by means of their enlarged antennae. Each time these are swept smartly downwards through the water they lift the tiny body upwards with a jerk. Since it is slightly heavier than the water it sinks a little during the recovery stroke, only to be jerked upwards once more on the next downward stroke. It is this jerky movement which was probably responsible originally for the name water flea.

Their method of feeding on algae and other minute organisms suspended in the water is similar to that used by the fairy shrimps. By their constant rhythmical movements the five pairs of thoracic phyllopods draw in a current of water. This is passed through barricades of bristles which filter out the food organisms, and then passes over thin exopodite gills which extract oxygen from it. The trapped food particles are then carried forward to the mouth in a separate current.

The reproductive habits of the water fleas are interesting. During most of the spring and summer only females are found, and they reproduce by parthenogenesis, laying eggs which develop without fertilization. Each female produces about twenty of these summer eggs at a time. They are placed in a space below the carapace above the hind end of the trunk. In this brood pouch they hatch in a few days as miniature replicas of the females which produced them, the nauplius larval stage being suppressed.

As autumn approaches, however, some of these eggs produce males, and at the same time some at least of the females produce a second kind of egg which will not develop until it has been fertilized. These winter eggs are bigger than the summer eggs, and contain an abundance of yolk. Each female produces only two or three of them, and when they are fertilized they also are placed in the brood pouch, which then proceeds to undergo a modification, its walls becoming much thickened. When the female next moults this ephippium, as it is called, with its contained eggs, falls to the bottom of the pond or lake. Here it lies dormant until the following spring, when its eggs at last hatch out as females, which themselves proceed to reproduce by parthenogenesis.

Production of males and winter eggs is probably connected with conditions, rather than being a rhythmical phenomenon occurring after a certain number of asexual generations. So long as these conditions are favourable parthenogenesis continues, but lack of food or deteriorating climatic conditions is believed to trigger off sexual reproduction. Normally such adverse conditions occur only with the approach of winter. In recent experimental work cultures of various cladocerans have maintained themselves for up to sixteen months under optimum conditions without once producing males or winter eggs. It was found possible, however, to induce them to do so by lowering the temperature, reducing the food supply, or allowing the culture to become overcrowded.

The water fleas are of great importance in the economy of lakes and ponds in which they are abundant. Since they feed on microscopic algae, and are themselves eaten by many other larger organisms, including fish, they play a leading role in the conversion of plant life into animal flesh. When conditions are good the algae multiply rapidly, and therefore so can the crustaceans which feed on them, thus providing an abundance of food for the larger animal life.

Fairy Shrimps and Water Fleas—

As already mentioned, the cladocerans are slightly heavier than water, and only prevent themselves from sinking to the bottom of the pond or lake by their constant jerky movements. These movements are carefully controlled so as to maintain them at different depths below the surface at different times of the day and night. At midday most of them will be found at some distance from the surface, and there will be very few in the upper layers. During the afternoon, however, there is a gradual upward migration, which continues after darkness has fallen until about midnight most of them will be found in the surface layers. At dawn a reverse downward migration begins, to reach its maximum around the middle of the day.

The reason for this regular vertical migration of the freshwater crustacean plankton is not known for certain, but as we shall see when we are discussing the marine Copepoda, similar migrations in the sea are related to corresponding migrations of the plant plankton on which they feed. It certainly does seem that intensity of light has some influence on these water-flea migrations. Another theory has been put forward that the migrations help to keep them well out in the lake. Lake water is always streaming in different directions at different depths, so that any organisms which remained at the same level would tend eventually to be deposited on the shore. By moving vertically they will pass from a current moving in one direction to currents moving in other directions, and so will tend to be kept away from the shore.

In British water there are a number of different species both of *Daphnia* and of *Simocephalus*. The two groups can be easily distinguished by a difference in the shape of the carapace. The hind end of the *Daphnia* carapace is extended as a short blunt spine, whereas in *Simocephalus* the hind end is rounded. The whole carapace, seen from the side, is rather more square in *Simocephalus*. Other British water fleas which should be mentioned are *Sida*, *Holopedium* and *Bosmina*. These are less common and less widespread than the other two kinds. Altogether there are ninety species of British fresh-water Cladocera. *Daphnia* and certain other Cladocera show an interesting respiratory adaptation when living in badly oxygenated stagnant waters. Haemoglobin develops in their blood, giving their whole bodies a reddish appearance and enabling them to make the maximum use of the limited oxygen supplies. There are a few species of marine Cladocera, but only two of these are at all common in British waters.

Together the water fleas constitute only one division of the sub-order Cladocera, the Calyptomera. Quite different from them in appearance and habits are the members of the other division, the Gymnomera. In these the carapace is reduced to a brood pouch which projects like a tiny balloon above the thorax. Although their thoracic limbs are not covered by the carapace, they are not used for swimming. As with the true water fleas, locomotion is provided for by the pair of well-developed antennae. In their feeding habits, too, they differ from the water fleas, having given up filtering minute organisms in favour of catching larger prey, including Rotifera and even Crustacea smaller than themselves.

The best-known British representative of the Gymnomera is *Leptodora kindti*, which with a length of about half an inch is the largest of the Cladocera. From its appearance no one would suspect its relationship with the typical water fleas. The whole body is very long and slender, due mainly to elongation of the head and the abdomen, the thorax, with its six pairs of limbs, being of normal length. It is with

these limbs that the creature captures its prey and conveys
it to its mouth. Like many of the Calyptomera, *Leptodora*
produces both summer and winter eggs. The latter hatch
in the spring as nauplius larvae, and are unique as the only
nauplii found in the Cladocera.

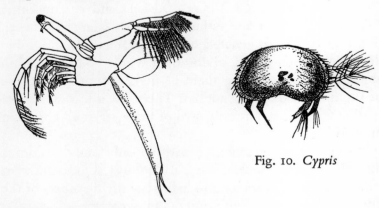

Fig. 10. *Cypris*

Fig. 9. *Leptodora kindti*

The second class of Crustacea, the Ostracoda, is a comparatively small group of tiny creatures somewhat similar
in general appearance to the water fleas. Like them, they
have short bodies completely enclosed in a bean-shaped
carapace. Unlike the carapace of the Cladocera, however, it
is hinged along the dorsal edge like the shell valves of a
mussel, the two halves being controlled by an adductor
muscle which joins them and is capable of pulling them
tightly together when it contracts. When danger threatens
the little creatures are able to withdraw all their limbs and
enclose themselves completely within their shells. Whereas
Daphnia, too, has a transparent shell enabling us to see all
its internal organs, the ostracod shell is relatively opaque,
so little of its body can be seen through it.

The Ostracoda are in the main fresh-water creatures,

though there are a few marine representatives. The best known and most widespread fresh-water kind is *Cypris*. Like *Daphnia* it swims by means of a pair of well-developed antennae. It does not, however, spend most of its time swimming as a member of the plankton, but instead walks about a good deal on the bottom of the pond or lake in which it lives, or among the branches of water plants. For this purpose it uses the first of its only two pairs of trunk limbs, the reduction of limbs having gone a good deal further in the Ostracoda than in the Cladocera. In fact they have a smaller number of limbs than any other group of Crustacea. The second pair seem to be incessantly sweeping the inside of the carapace, as though keeping it clean. It seems unlikely that the carapace really needs such continuous cleaning, but no one has yet discovered what other purpose this movement might serve. These two pairs of thoracic appendages lack gills, and they do not filter food organisms. Feeding is done by the various appendages of the head, the food consisting mainly of dead organic matter.

Reproductive habits among the Ostracoda vary according to the species. In some both sexes are equally represented, and reproduction is normal, whereas in others no males have ever been found, so presumably there is permanent parthenogenesis. In contrast to most crustaceans ostracods do not carry their eggs about with them until they hatch, but deposit them in clusters on water plants. These clusters are fairly easy to find because of their orange colour. There is evidence that ostracod eggs can remain viable in mud even though it dries up, and there are records of ostracod eggs developing normally after having been inbedded in dried-up mud for up to thirty years. The nauplius larvae which hatch from the eggs are unusual in that they have already have tiny bivalve shells.

Fairy Shrimps and Water Fleas

Like the Cladocera, the Ostracoda are important members of the fresh-water fauna, occurring in particularly large numbers in very weedy ponds. Altogether there are eighty-eight British fresh-water species. They are all small creatures, none exceeding a length of about one-tenth of an inch. There are only a few marine representatives, and these are never prominent in the plankton. In contrast to the Branchiopoda and Ostracoda, the members of the other four classes of Crustacea are principally marine creatures with a minority of fresh-water representatives.

3 · The Copepods

Any representative sample of the smaller animal life of a pond or a lake will almost certainly contain a considerable proportion of copepods, tiny creatures of similar size to the water fleas, but very distinctive in appearance. Best known and most numerous of the 105 British fresh-water species are the various species of *Cyclops*. Together the Copepoda and the Cladocera constitute the major portion of the plankton of lakes and ponds, and are therefore an important item in the diet of fish and other fresh-water animals.

Cyclops has a pear- or club-shaped body. The front of the broad part of the body consists of all the head segments and

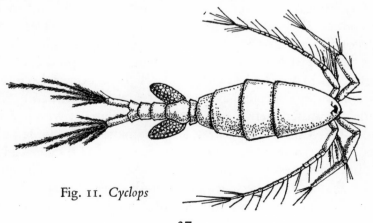

Fig. 11. *Cyclops*

37

the first two thoracic segments fused together, but in common with all the copepods there is no carapace. The remainder of the broad part comprises thoracic segments 3, 4 and 5. Behind it is the narrow hind part of the body consisting of the last thoracic and four abdominal segments, these being followed by a forked telson bearing exceptionally long feathery bristles.

Compound eyes are absent, as they are in all the Copepoda, but the median eye is well developed and prominent, being usually red or black in colour. The antennules are exceptionally long, and in the male they can be bent in the form of hooks with which the female is held during mating. The antennae are much shorter and uniramous, in contrast to the condition in most other crustacea where the antennae are biramous and much better developed than the antennules. Another unusual feature of *Cyclops* is its method of feeding. It has abandoned the filter method commonly employed by so many small planktonic Crustacea, and instead seizes small particles with its limbs, passing them to its mouth. It is also believed to feed on the bodies of small dead animals. Two methods of swimming are employed. Rhythmical movements of the antennules and antennae produce slow movement, but for swifter progress the second to the fifth pairs of thoracic limbs are employed.

A conspicuous feature of most female Copepoda is a pair of egg sacs attached to either side of the abdominal region, though some species have only one such sac. At mating the males transfer their spermatozoa to the females wrapped in sacs called spermatophores. These remain inside the female egg duct, so that the eggs can be fertilized as they are laid. They then pass into the egg sacs where they remain until they hatch. In some species two kinds of eggs are produced at different times, one developing immediately while the

The Copepods

other is a resting kind designed to survive during unfavourable periods, developing only when conditions improve.

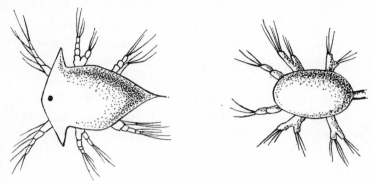

Fig. 12.
(a) A typical crustacean nauplius larva.   (b) The Cirripede nauplius

In its development the *Cyclops* egg shows a very full series of larval stages. It hatches as a nauplius larva, which has already been mentioned on several occasions, but has not yet been described. Its body is more or less oval or kite-shaped, with the broad end forward, and carries three pairs of appendages well furnished with bristles. The first pair is uniramous, and will eventually become the antennules. The next two are both biramous, and represent the antennae and mandibles. None of these have yet acquired their adult function, their role in the larvae being to propel them through the water. As they grow these nauplii moult frequently, and at each moult a little more is added to the hind end, each addition representing one or more of the adult segments. These larvae with varying numbers of head and thoracic segments behind the original three of the nauplius are known as metanauplii.

Finally comes a moult which involves a drastic change of shape, the next stage looking much like a miniature adult, but not having the full number of segments. This is the first copepodid or *Cyclops* larva, and is followed at succeeding moults by four more. The fifth finally moults to produce the adult complete with all its segments and appendages.

In addition to the various species of *Cyclops*, representatives of two other types of Copepoda are commonly present in our lakes and ponds. Species of *Diaptomus* are related to the all-important marine form *Calanus*. Their antennules are exceptionally long, often nearly equal in length to the whole body, and they can be further distinguished from *Cyclops* species by the fact that the females carry only one egg sac. Unlike *Cyclops*, too, they obtain their food supplies by filtering minute organisms from the water. Throughout the winter they remain plentiful, some species in fact being present in greater numbers then than in the summer.

Much smaller than the other types are a group of Harpacticoida, most of which are less than one-twenty-fifth of an inch long. They have head and thorax fused together, and there is no obvious external indication to distinguish them from the abdomen. They are thus for Crustacea unusually worm-like in general appearance, and also unusual in that their antennules and antennae are small and inconspicuous. Unlike *Cyclops* and its relatives they are not capable of swimming, but spend their time creeping about the bottom of the pond or lake and over the water plants. Although their habits make them less likely to be found, they are nevertheless quite a large group, with no fewer than forty-six British species, the most abundant being *Canthocamptus staphylinus*. They are present in greater numbers in the winter than in the summer, and it is in the winter that the females will be found carrying their single-egg cases.

The Copepods

Fresh-water Cladocera and Copepoda sometimes act as intermediate hosts for certain vertebrate parasites. *Cyclops*, for example, harbours one of the stages in the life history of a particular tapeworm, *Schistocephalus gasterostei*, the adult form of which lives in the digestive system of birds. Any eggs which find their way into fresh water hatch into free-swimming larvae. These can only develop further if they bore their way into a *Cyclops*. Here each forms a resting cyst, which is incapable of developing unless the *Cyclops* is eaten by a fish, when it again becomes active and gives rise to the next stage of development. This stage forms another cyst in the body cavity of the fish. Again development comes to a halt, and can only be completed if the fish is eaten by a bird, when the larva within the cyst finally produces an adult tapeworm.

Daphnia also harbours intermediate stages in the life history of other parasites which attacks ducks and other water-birds when they eat the infected *Daphnia*. The infection of valuable ducks by such parasites became a problem at Whipsnade as their collection grew, and was solved by an ingenious method. Fish were introduced into the ponds to keep them clear of *Daphnia*. Thus deprived of their intermediate hosts, the parasites died out.

Despite their relative abundance in fresh water, the Copepoda are principally marine creatures. In all the seas of the world they are the dominant animals of the plankton, occurring in numbers so fantastic that it seems probable that the total number of individuals exceeds the total number of all other multicellular animals put together, including land as well as aquatic animals, and not forgetting the amazing abundance of insects.

The Copepoda are divided into three groups. The Harpacticoida which we have already met are a small group of

The Copepods

exclusively fresh-water forms. The other two groups are the Podoplea, to which both the fresh-water forms like *Cyclops* belong, as well as certain free-living marine forms and an important group of marine parasites; and the Gymnoplea, the dominant group which contains *Calanus* and a great variety of incredibly abundant marine planktonic forms.

Calanus and its gymnoplean relatives are more primitive in their structure and habits than *Cyclops* and the free-living Podoplea. Their antennae have retained the biramous condition typical of crustacea generally, and only one thoracic segment has become fused with the head. They feed, too, on microscopic organisms strained from the water by fringes of bristles on the antennae, mandibles and maxillae.

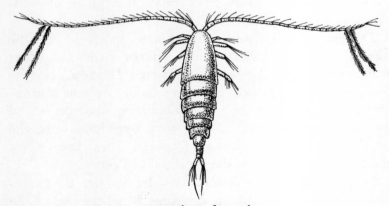

Fig. 13. *Calanus finmarchicus*

One of the largest of the Gymnoplea to be found in British waters is *Calanus finmarchicus*, an extremely important member of the plankton because it forms the principal food of the herring. Whereas most planktonic Copepoda are not much larger than a pin's head, *Calanus finmarchicus* is about the size of a rice grain, but in other respects is typical of the group to which it belongs. Its head contains the usual five pairs of appendages. In addition the first thoracic segment is fused with it, and its appendages are modified as additional feeding organs. The remaining five thoracic appendages are typical biramous appendages flattened as swimming paddles. The thin abdomen consists of only four short segments devoid of limbs, and in the female the first two are fused together, so that there are apparently only three abdominal segments. The telson bears on each side five feathery bristles.

Normally *Calanus* lies vertically in the water, with its head uppermost and its long feathery antennules extended on either side. They help to prevent the body, which is slightly heavier than sea water, from sinking too rapidly. To move gently upwards the little creature is able to use its antennae, but if it needs to move faster the last five pairs of thoracic limbs are brought into play. As we shall see in the next chapter, upward movement is a very important feature in the life of all the marine planktonic Copepoda.

In their reproductive habits the Gymnoplea are very similar to *Cyclops*. At mating the males transfer their spermatozoa in spermatophores to the female egg duct, where they are retained to fertilize the eggs as they travel down to be laid. In some species, of *Centropages* for example, the last thoracic limb is modified as a pair of forceps for transferring the spermatophore, and the right antennule is hinged to form a clasping organ with which the male can hold the female during the transfer. The fertilized eggs may be retained in two egg sacs until they hatch, or they may be attached to the abdomen in a cluster. In many species the eggs are brightly coloured in a beautiful translucent emerald, sapphire or deep blue. In Arctic waters *Calanus* species breed only once a year, but in our seas there are usually three or four generations a year. During the winter the majority of species remain in the fifth and last copepodid stage. This moults to the adult stage in February, and then proceeds to reproduce. Its offspring become mature and breed in May, and the next two generations breed in July and September, the over-wintering copepodid stages resulting from this last reproduction.

The largest of all the European Gymnoplea is *Euchaeta norvegica*, which lives in deeper water than the majority of the other species, being most common off the coast of Norway and in some of the fiords, but can also be found in deep water off the west coast of Scotland and in Loch Fyne. It is an exceptionally beautiful creature, with a general body colour of rose-red, deep blue eggs and iridescent tail plumes which show all the colours of the rainbow. During the day-time it can be found as far down as sixty fathoms, coming nearer to the surface at night, when it has the added attraction of being luminous.

The overwhelming majority of planktonic Copepoda are Gymnoplea, but there are some representatives of the Podoplea in the surface waters. These are similar to *Cyclops* in general appearance. The most important marine Podoplea, however, are a group of parasites, some of which infect various kinds of fish, while others attack invertebrates. These show varying degrees of degeneration in adaptation to their special mode of life. Least modified of them all is *Caligus*, an ectoparasite which lives mainly in the gill chambers of fishes, sucking blood from the gill filaments with a specially modified suctorial mouth. It is, however, capable of leaving one host and swimming about in the sea until it locates another. Both sexes are similar, and show little signs of degeneration.

Chondracanthus, on the other hand, shows considerable modification. Like *Caligus* it is a gill parasite, but is so degenerate that it cannot leave its host. In the adult female the appendages are very degenerate, and the body is reduced to a mass of flesh produced into a number of paired lobes,

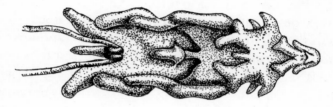

Fig. 14. *Chondracanthus*

the whole structure bearing no real resemblance to a crustacean. The males are much smaller and less degenerate, but remain permanently attached to the females by their antennae, which have become modified as hooks for the purpose.

Fig. 15. *Lernaea*. (a) Female with the much smaller male attached to its abdomen. (b) Final degenerate stage of female, as found attached to the gill filaments of its fish host

Lernaea is yet another gill parasite in which the adult female exhibits extreme degeneration, though only after a rather complex life history. The eggs hatch as normal nauplii, which continue development until the first copepodid stage, when they become parasitic on the gills of flatfish, developing a suctorial mouth with which they obtain food from the host tissues. The body now loses much of its crustacean character, entering into what has been described as a pupal stage, in which all power of movement is lost.

The Copepods

After a while, however, the ability to swim is regained, and the larvae leave their hosts as adult copepods. Mating now takes place, and is the end of the road for the much smaller males, which do not develop further. The females, however, now seek out members of the cod family and attach themselves to the gill filaments. Here major degeneration occurs, the head anchoring itself permanently to the host by sending processes deep into its tissues. Remnants of the thoracic appendages remain, but are functionless, while the remainder of the body develops into a relatively enormous twisted worm-like sac which eventually produces great quantities of eggs.

Whereas with most parasites it is the adult stage which is parasitic, in *Monstrilla* the adults of both sexes are free-swimming and normal Crustacea in external appearance. The nauplius larvae, however, enter into the bodies of various worms, from which they absorb nourishment by means of modified antennae. In this state the larval life is completed, and when a last moult produces the adults, they work their way out of their hosts to live a free life. They are not completely normal, however, for they lack both mouth appendages and gut. All the food they require for the complete life cycle is absorbed during their parasitic larval life.

Closely related to the Copepoda are the members of the fourth crustacean class, the Branchiura or carp-lice. Until recently they were classed as one of the Copepod orders, but the differences between them and the rest of the copepods makes it advisable to classify them separately. They are all temporary parasites on fish where they may be found attached to almost any part of the body. In structure they are perfectly adapted to their mode of life. A few species are marine, but the majority are fresh-water creatures, most of them belonging to the genus *Argulus*.

The Copepods

Unlike the Copepoda they possess well-developed compound eyes. The mouth is specially modified for sucking blood, and the maxillules bear a pair of powerful suckers with which they can attach themselves to their hosts. The whole body is extremely flattened so as to offer the minimum of resistance as the host swims rapidly through the water. Only four pairs of thoracic appendages are represented, but these are biramous and well developed for

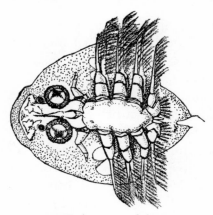

Fig. 16. *Argulus*, one of the carp-lice

swimming. The abdomen is much reduced, unsegmented and without limbs. The fertilized eggs are not retained in an egg sac, but deposited on stones, where they remain until they hatch. There are no larval stages, the eggs producing tiny creatures essentially similar to the adults in structure.

The most common British species is *Argulus foliaceus*, in which the larger females are about a quarter of an inch in length. This and other species are found on almost every species of fresh-water fish, and they are much more common than is generally realized.

4 · *The Pastures of the Sea*

The teeming animal life of the plankton provides all the food needed by the larger animal life of the seas and the sea-shore, including the fishes. The planktonic Crustacea, and especially the Copepoda, constitute a high proportion of this animal plankton, so this seems to be the appropriate place to consider the exact place occupied by these animals in the economy of the seas.

On land all animal life ultimately depends on the plants. They alone are able to build up from simple raw materials the complex carbohydrates and other substances which constitute the food of the animal kingdom. Herbivorous animals feed directly on the plants, but the carnivores are no less dependent upon them. The animals which they eat are either herbivores or have in their turn fed on herbivores. There may be several links in the food chain, but always the animals at the bottom of the chain are plant eaters, and it is through them that the carnivores higher up the chain ultimately derive their food from the plant kingdom.

The same principle holds for marine and sea-shore life, the main difference being that whereas land plants are complex and visible, the marine plants are minute and individually invisible except under the microscope. Only the seaweeds are large, but these are not very important as a source of food for marine animals.

The Pastures of the Sea

These minute plants are called diatoms, and it is to their swarming in the surface layers that the sea owes its green colour. Long before the invention of the microscope revealed the full truth of his statement, Pliny had written: 'Nature is nowhere more perfect than in her smaller works.' The diatoms are certainly outstanding examples of nature's perfect workmanship.

Each diatom consists of a single cell containing chlorophyll and surrounded by a transparent case or shell of silica. This is made in two halves, one fitting on the other as a lid fits on a box. In many species these shells are beautifully shaped, with slender processes projecting outwards into the water. Once it has been formed, the shell cannot be increased in size. When the diatom begins to outgrow its shell, it divides to form two new diatoms, each of which takes one half of the old shell and forms a new half to go with it. The new half is always made slightly smaller than the old half, which serves as the lid of the new shell. Hence with repeated divisions the members of a diatom population get progressively smaller. This cannot go on indefinitely, however, because when a certain minimum size is reached deformities begin to appear. To counteract this the diatoms undergo an interesting process of rejuvenation. The shells are discarded, and the now naked auxospore, as it is called, proceeds to grow until it has become several times larger and has thus restored the maximum size for the species. Now two new shell valves are constructed. Different diatom species undergo rejuvenation at different intervals. Many do so once a year in July or August, whereas others seem to make do with a rejuvenation once every two or three years.

Diatoms are confined to the surface waters of the sea, where alone they can get sufficient sunlight to carry on photosynthesis. Here they multiply rapidly and provide the

D   49

pastures on which the members of the animal plankton feed. These plankton animals can be divided into two groups, the permanent and the temporary. The former consist of numbers of tiny animals, mostly Crustacea, which live the whole of their lives drifting in the surface waters. The temporary animal plankton consists of the larvae of all those shore and marine animals whose young stages lead a drifting existence before settling down to their adult habitats, the eggs and young stages of the majority of fishes, together with of course the young stages of the members of the permanent plankton. The temporary plankton is subject to very large seasonal variations, reaching its peak in the spring, which is the breeding season for most species, and falling to a very low level by the late autumn.

The members of the animal plankton, both temporary and permanent, depend upon the diatoms for their food supply. Some of them are herbivorous, feeding directly on the diatoms, while others are carnivorous, feeding on these herbivores. The fish and other larger marine animals in their turn obtain their food directly or indirectly from the animal plankton. Hence a knowledge of the factors controlling the diatom populations is the essential basis for an understanding of the whole economy of the seas. This explains why so much of the fisheries research which has taken place over the past seventy years or so has been devoted to investigations of the diatoms and the animal plankton rather than to the fish themselves.

The abundance of diatoms in the surface waters varies considerably at different times of the year. These variations form a well-defined cycle which has been the subject of a good deal of investigation. As with land plants, diatom growth is most rapid in the spring and summer and much reduced in winter. By about the end of February the spring diatom outburst begins, and reaches its maximum in April, when the diatoms are growing and reproducing so fast that the population is doubling its weight every twenty-four hours. This does not mean, however, that the total number of diatoms in the sea is increasing at this rate, because at the same time enormous numbers of plankton animals which graze on them are also hatching out, and they eat the diatoms almost as fast as they are being produced.

The high level of the diatom production achieved in April is maintained until July, when it begins to fall during the rest of the summer; for a few weeks in the autumn there is a second outburst before it finally dies down for the winter.

Although they are so small the diatoms are produced in such vast numbers that it has been calculated that the yearly crop in the English Channel amounts to some $5\frac{1}{2}$ tons to every acre. It is interesting to compare this with the average yield of hay per acre on the land of $1\frac{1}{2}$ tons, or 3 to 4 tons in a good year from two crops. It has been estimated that 0·06 per cent of the total diatom crop is harvested as fish by the fishing-fleets.

The factors controlling diatom growth are similar to those which regulate the growth of land plants. Like land plants, they can only flourish if they have adequate supplies of mineral salts, especially nitrates and phosphates. It is the fluctuations in the available quantities of these which are responsible for the regular spring and autumn outbursts and the midsummer decline.

During the winter, when there is little sunshine and temperatures are low, there is little or no diatom growth, so stocks of phosphate and nitrate accumulate in the sea. They result from the decay of plant and animal material, in the same way as the mineral salts in the soil are replenished by decaying humus. Thus when the warmer spring weather approaches, with its increasing amounts of sunshine, there is an abundance of salts to support rapid diatom growth. The great rate of diatom growth from April onwards gradually depletes these stocks, so that by July they are becoming scarce. This leads to the summer decline in the diatom population. By this time, incidentally, most of the members of the temporary plankton have completed their planktonic life, so that the reduced diatom population has a reduced population, consisting mainly of the permanent plankton, to support.

The short autumn outburst is also related to phosphate and nitrate supplies, and begins just after the onset of the usual autumn gales. During the summer the upper 60 feet or so of the sea become warmed by the sun until they are several degrees warmer than the water below. Where the two layers meet there is a discontinuity layer or thermocline, which effectively prevents much mixing between them. Meanwhile in the lower layer phosphates and nitrates are being continually released by the decay of dead organisms, and accumulate because the water is too far below the surface for diatoms to live and use them up. The autumn gales, however, disturb the water sufficiently to break down the discontinuity layer, so that some of the deeper water comes up towards the surface, making its phosphates and nitrates available for a renewed outburst of diatom growth.

Soon after this the diminishing light intensity and falling temperatures reduce diatom growth to a minimum. Most of the diatoms which survive the winter do so in the form of resting spores surrounded by a thick wall of silica. It is these which revive towards the end of February to initiate the spring outburst.

The Pastures of the Sea

Because the diatoms are the basis of all food chains in the sea, any factor which affects the diatom population can affect the animal populations, including the fish. Some interesting experiments conducted in Scotland demonstrated very convincingly the importance of phosphates and nitrates for diatom growth, and the consequent effects on the growth of fish. An arm of a sea-water loch was dammed off from the rest of the loch and large quantities of nitrate and phosphate added from time to time. The result was a great increase in the diatoms, maintained through the year, and a corresponding increase in the animal plankton which obtained their food directly or indirectly from them. There was, too, a profound effect on the growth rate of young fish in the loch. In less than a year young plaice had grown as large as a normal two- or three-year-old fish, while in two years young flounders had made as much growth as they would normally have made in six years. These results are particularly significant, because plaice and flounders do not themselves feed on the animal plankton. Their food consists of bivalve molluscs which feed on the animals in the plankton, these in their turn having consumed the diatoms. The experiments were repeated later in another arm of the loch not dammed off from the rest, and very similar results were obtained.

One interesting fact connected with the ultimate dependence of the fish populations on the diatoms is that the vitamin A which makes cod- and halibut-liver oil so valuable to us comes from the diatoms. Neither the cod nor the halibut, nor any of the intermediate animals in the food chain, is able to make the vitamin itself. It is made by the diatoms and passes from each member of the chain to the next.

Because they are plants needing sunlight for photosynthesis, the diatoms can only live in the surface waters where the sunlight is able to penetrate. They are, however, slightly more dense than sea water and have no means of locomotion. This is the explanation for the various projections on their shells. They are not ornaments, but anti-sinking devices which increase their resistance to the water and retard the rate at which they sink. With their aid the continual movements of the water are sufficient to keep the diatoms suspended near the surface.

The plankton contains some other important single-celled organisms which also provide food for the small crustacea and the other plankton animals. Second only in importance to the diatoms as basic food organisms are the Dinoflagellata, a group in some respects on the very border line between animal and plant life. Many behave like perfectly good animals, feeding on organic matter, particularly the diatoms, and thus form the second link in many food chains. Others, however, are much more like plants, containing chlorophyll and other pigments which enable them to nourish themselves by photosynthesis. These form alternatives to the diatoms as first links in food chains.

Although, like the diatoms, only consisting of a single cell, they are in general rather larger. Like the diatoms, too, they present a variety of delicate shapes, also probably designed to help keep them suspended, though they do have their own means of locomotion. Most of them are covered with a thin transparent shell consisting of a number of plates fitting accurately together. They are provided with two whip-like flagella with which they can propel themselves through the water to a limited extent. In tropical seas they are much more abundant than they are in our seas, and sometimes replace the diatoms as the most important basic food.

Economically the dinoflagellates are important as the

principal food of the sardine or pilchard, and as an important item in the diet of the oyster. Many of them are phosphorescent, and swarms of them are the main cause of phosphorescence in temperate seas. One of them, called *Noctiluca* (shine-by-night), is particularly bright. As it swarms in its millions, it is capable of producing a wonderful display. Under the microscope it looks rather like an apple, complete with a stalk. In a dense swarm there may be as many as 25,000 of them in a cubic foot of water.

Two more groups of single-celled organisms deserve mention, the Foraminifera and the Radiolaria. Both belong to the animal kingdom and feed on diatoms, thus forming the second links in many food chains. The former have beautiful coiled shells made of calcium carbonate, and looking like microscopic snail shells. The Radiolaria inhabit spherical- and goblet-shaped shells perforated with numerous holes and looking under the microscope like some exquisite Chinese carvings. These, like the diatom shells, are made of silica. Both groups lack any means of locomotion, but need to keep in the surface water to feed on the diatoms. Instead of projections on their shells, their anti-sinking devices consist of threads of living tissue which radiate out from the shells into the water.

These various single-celled organisms of the plankton have another claim to importance besides forming the basis of marine food chains. Although they are among the smallest of living things, they have played a great part in building up the earth's crust. When they die they sink to the bottom of the sea; their bodies decay but their shells remain, forming accumulations called oozes. Such accumulations from the remote past have become fossilized as rock. Thus chalk contains large numbers of fossilized Foraminifera shells. Many other rocks, some of which now provide building stone, also contain the fossilized remains of these various animals and plants.

It has been estimated that no less than 48 million square miles of the present ocean bed are covered with a layer of the accumulated shells of Foraminifera many yards thick. The commonest species of Foraminifera belong to the group called *Globigerina*, and the *Globigerina* oozes account for the majority of the 48 million square miles.

In some parts of the world the silica skeletons of the diatoms have been fossilized not as solid rock but as layers of siliceous earths which may be 100 feet or more in thickness. These earths have important commercial uses. They are used because of their abrasive properties as the basis of certain silver polishes and tooth pastes. One type of siliceous earth, known as Kieselguhr, is mixed with nitro-glycerine to make dynamite. It is interesting to reflect that many of the large buildings in towns all over the world, the Egyptian pyramids, the white cliffs of Dover and the fish we eat are among the things we owe to the diatoms and the other minute plankton organisms.

One unsolved mystery surrounds the animals of the plankton. They all perform regular vertical migrations every twenty-four hours. By midday they are at their lowest depths, which for some species may be several hundred feet below the surface. During the afternoon they gradually come up nearer the surface, and by midnight they have nearly all come up into the surface layers. We have already seen that *Calanus* is able to swim actively by means of its thoracic limbs. Experiments have shown that in the space of an hour it can rise 50 feet, but in a short two-minute burst swimming at maximum speed it can actually climb at a rate equivalent to more than 200 feet an hour. When swimming downwards, as might be expected, these speeds can be exceeded. Over a period of one hour *Calanus* can sink at least 150 feet, and in a short burst at full speed can dive at a rate equivalent to 330 feet an hour. That these regular vertical migrations occur in all animals of the plankton is an accepted fact. But why they occur is still a mystery. Various suggestions have been put forward, but none seem to be very convincing.

The vertical migrations of *Calanus*, however, have dictated the methods used to catch herrings. As the multitudes of *Calanus* come up into the surface waters at night, the herrings which feed on them follow suit. Hence it is that the herring fishermen shoot their drift nets at night. Drifting during the day-time would yield very few fish.

5 · *The Barnacles*

In any group of animals it is not unusual to find some
members so modified in structure in adaptation to some
special mode of life that it is difficult or impossible to recognize them as belonging to the group. Often these aberrant
species are parasites. The barnacles, which make up the fifth
class of Crustacea, the Cirrepedia, are exceptional in that

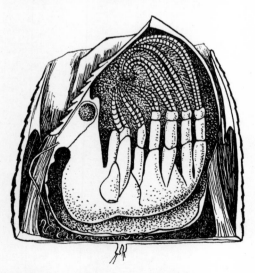

Fig. 17. An acorn barnacle, with side plates removed to show
the structure of the animal lying within them

The Barnacles

every member is so different in the adult stage from any normal crustacean that no one would suspect their true relationships without a knowledge of their development.

The most common of all the cirripedes are the sea-shore acorn barnacles, little cones of shell firmly fixed to almost every rock, and often present in incredible numbers. Anyone seeing them for the first time might be forgiven for believing them to be some kind of miniature limpet. The shell itself consists of six vertical calcareous plates firmly fixed together to form the side walls, leaving a space at the top covered with a further four hinged plates. Inside is a short body bearing six pairs of distinctly curved biramous appendages, each well supplied with long bristles. These can be thrust out into the water by opening up the four roof plates. Their function is to collect diatoms and other minute plankton organisms, which they do when they are covered by the continuous sweeping motion of an incoming tide. The collected food is pulled into the shell and conveyed to the mouth. The appendages represent the six pairs of thoracic limbs. Nothing remains of the abdomen, and little of the head, except the mouth.

To be unable to move, being firmly cemented to a rock, and to have to rely for food upon such microscopic organisms as the returning tide may bring within reach, having no means of capturing larger prey, hardly suggests a flourishing mode of life. Yet the little acorn barnacles which endure this apparently limited existence are among the most successful of all shore animals. On an exposed rocky shore they may be more numerous than any other animals. It has been estimated that there may be more than 1,000 million of them along a single mile stretch.

Many sedentary marine animals merely shed their reproductive products into the sea at the breeding season, fertilization of the eggs being a random process made reasonably sure on account of the huge numbers of eggs and spermatozoa shed into the same volume of water. With the acorn barnacles, however, mating occurs. Each individual is hermaphrodite, but self-fertilization does not take place. Instead each individual deposits its spermatozoa within the shell of a neighbour by means of an extensible penis. The eggs are retained within the shell until they hatch as typical nauplius larvae, distinguished from the nauplii of other crustacean groups only by the fact that the front edge is extended laterally into a pair of short horns. After several moults the last nauplius is succeeded by what is known as a cypris larva, on account of its superficial resemblance to the ostrocod *Cypris*. It has a pair of tiny hinged shells, six pairs of thoracic appendages and well-developed antennules.

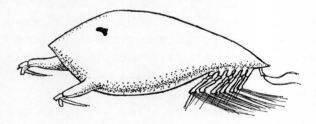

Fig. 18. Cirripede cypris larva

The cypris larva does not feed, for its function in the barnacle life history is to find a suitable spot for the future adult to spend its life, and to fix itself there securely. This settling is no haphazard business. A larva may search the rock surface for upwards of an hour before it finds a suitable position. Having done so, it then stands upon its head, bringing its large antennules in contact with the rock. They, in fact, are connected with a pair of cement glands in the head which now secrete an adhesive liquid which soon dries

The Barnacles

on contact with the sea water. In this way the larva fixes itself securely to its chosen position.

Further changes now convert it to an adult. The head degenerates completely except for the mouth, and the abdomen is likewise completely obliterated. At the same time the thorax becomes tipped over as it were on to its back, so that the six pairs of now well-developed appendages point upwards just beneath the four lid plates.

When the cypris larvae first settle they always do so along the flow of the tide, so that they face up or down the shore. Before finally cementing themselves down, however, they turn through 90 degrees, and in doing so ensure that their food net of limbs will always be set across the water flowing on the incoming or outgoing tides. In this way they ensure filtering the maximum amount of water and so trapping the maximum amount of food.

When the tide goes out the lid plates are closed, trapping some water and a bubble of air which will enable the animal to remain moist and go on breathing until the tide returns. In hot weather a curious scraping or hissing noise can sometimes be heard around rocks covered with acorn barnacles. It is made as thousands of individuals press their lid plates tightly against one another to prevent the water evaporating.

Like other shore animals, the acorn barnacles occupy a zone whose upper and lower limits are respectively determined by their ability to endure exposure to the air and immersion in water. Larvae which settle on rocks above or below the limits of this zone will not survive. The position of a barnacle within its zone has a profound effect on its life. Those which settle low down the shore grow more quickly and reach maturity at the end of a year, usually dying after three years. Those living in the upper part of the zone, however, do not spawn until they are two years old, and generally survive for five. These differences are directly connected with the food supply. The barnacles lower down the shore are covered with water for a longer time each day than those higher up, and therefore catch more food because they have a longer time to feed.

Acorn barnacles are very sensitive to the action of waves, and their distribution varies according to whether the shore on which they are living is sheltered or exposed to heavy seas. On an open shore they not only grow more quickly than at corresponding levels on a sheltered shore, but the upper and lower limits of their zone are extended. There are probably two reasons for these effects. The greater water movement in rougher waters means more passing through the food nets, and therefore more food trapped, so that the barnacles grow more quickly at all levels and can live higher up the shore, where in calmer waters insufficient food would be obtained.

It is not so easy to explain why rough water should enable them to live lower down the shore. Most true shore animals are so adapted to an intertidal life that a period of exposure to the air is as necessary to them as a period of immersion in the water. This is probably true of the barnacles. Perhaps the heavy surf on an exposed shore carries enough air down to them when they are covered to enable them to make do with shorter periods of complete exposure to the air than they would require in calmer seas.

Acorn barnacles grow mostly in the spring and late summer. It seems that temperatures are too high in midsummer and too low in winter for rapid growth. During the summer the shells of first-year barnacles, and the new growth at the base of the shell plates of older specimens, appear pure white, whereas the shell laid down in previous years is greenish brown. The reason for this is that during the autumn spores of certain tiny algae settle on the white shell and germinate, growing right into the shell substance and changing its colour. Apparently these algae do no harm to the barnacles. They may in fact help to supply them with oxygen. When the sun shines on the water numerous oxygen bubbles can sometimes be seen streaming up from the shell, the result of photosynthesis in the algae.

The majority of the acorn barnacles found on British shores belong to two species, and although it is not easy to distinguish between them, they provide a good illustration of the effects of sea temperature in controlling the distribution of animals. As far as sea-shore and marine life is concerned the British Isles are very favourably placed. While the majority of species belong to the north temperate group, our western and south-western shores are washed by the warmer waters of the North Atlantic Drift or Gulf Stream. As a result, we find there quite a number of representatives of the lusitanean or Mediterranean group, which are animals whose main areas of distribution are farther south. Of the two barnacles one, called *Balanus balanoides*, is a north temperate species while the other, *Chthamalus stellatus*, is lusitanean.

Temperature affects an animal's northern and southern limits of distribution in two ways. The adults of each species are adapted for life within a certain temperature range. Too far south it becomes too warm for them to survive, and too far north too cold. There is a second temperature range outside which they cannot breed, and this often has much narrower limits than the survival range, so that an animal may be absent from an area where it could live because it is too warm or too cold for it to breed.

On our south-western shores, where the two barnacles

both flourish, *Balanus* is living at the extreme southern limits of its range, and *Chthamalus* at the extreme northern limits. This has an interesting effect on their breeding. Most marine and sea-shore animals are so adapted that they begin to spawn when the water reaches a certain temperature, and will then continue so long as temperatures remain within the breeding range. The initial temperature acts as a sort of trigger which sets off the breeding mechanism. For a north temperate species this necessary initial temperature, like the breeding range, is considerably lower than for a lusitanean species. In the south-west the initial breeding temperature for *Balanus balanoides* occurs in mid-winter, for it is a very northerly north temperate species, so that by the late spring its larvae are ready to settle. The initial breeding temperature for *Chthamalus*, however, is not attained until midsummer, so that its larvae are not ready to settle on the rocks until the autumn. Farther south temperatures would remain too high all the year round to stimulate *Balanus* to breeding activity, while on our east and north-east coasts the temperature necessary to stimulate *Chthamalus* to breed would never be reached.

Mention must be made of three other British species of acorn barnacles, none of which are anything like so abundant as the two species we have been dealing with. *Balanus perforatus* occurs on the lower parts of the shore and extends into the shallow offshore waters, the region known as the sub-littoral zone. *Balanus crenatus* is an entirely sub-littoral species, which may be occasionally exposed at extremely low spring tides. It often settles on pier piles in large numbers. The third species, *Balanus improvisus*, is adapted to life in brackish water, and is consequently confined to estuaries.

Closely related to the acorn barnacles is the stalked ship's barnacle, *Lepas anatifera*. Like the various acorn barnacles it

The pea crab, *Pinnotheres pisum*, which often lives for protection in mussel shells

The edible crab, *Cancer pagurus*

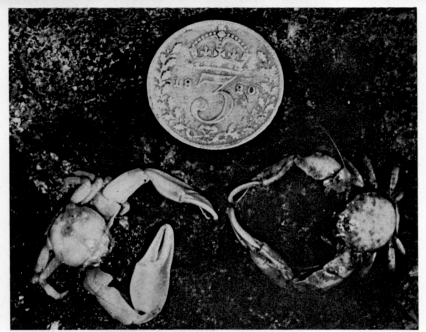

The smooth porcelain crab, *Porcellana longicornis*, is the smallest of all British crabs. It can often be found on the shore clinging to the undersides of stones

The hairy porcelain crab, *Porcellana platycheles*. Its relatively large flattened claws and its legs are fringed with hairs, to which mud and sand cling to give the creature a dirty appearance and make it difficult to detect

The thornback spider crab, *Maia maia*, is the largest of the British spider crabs

Underside of another common spider crab, *Hyas araneus*. The wide apron shows that this is a female

The common sea-slater, *Ligea oceanica*, is a large relative of the terrestrial woodlice. During the daytime it hides away in crevices near the top of the shore, coming out to feed at night when there is less danger of being attacked by its enemies

Underneath view of a thornback spider crab. This one is a male, as shown by its narrow apron

The crawfish or spiny lobster, *Palinurus vulgaris*. Its claws are very much smaller than those of the

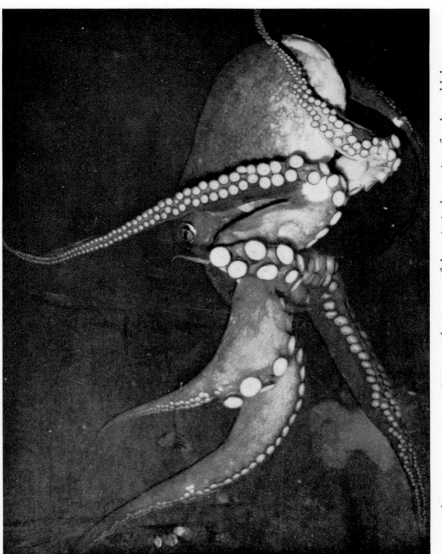

The common octopus, *Octopus vulgaris*, one of the principal enemies of crabs and lobsters

The stalked or ship's barnacle, *Lepas anatifera*, is commonly found attached to driftwood and objects washed up on the shore. Five plates cover the thorax, and the head is represented by the long fleshy stalk

A mass of small one-year-old acorn barnacles, *Balanus balanoides*, attached to an exposed rock surface. Some will eventually die to provide space for the growth of the others

A common green shore crab, *Carcinus maenas*, with a mass of young acorn barnacles growing on its carapace. It will lose these when it next moults

A common shore crab parasitized by a specimen of the sac barnacle, *Sacculina carcini*, seen here, bulging out between the crab's body and its apron

The velvet fiddler crab, *Portunus puber*, the largest of our swimming crabs. It is covered with a rich brown hair-like velvety pile, and has bright red eyes

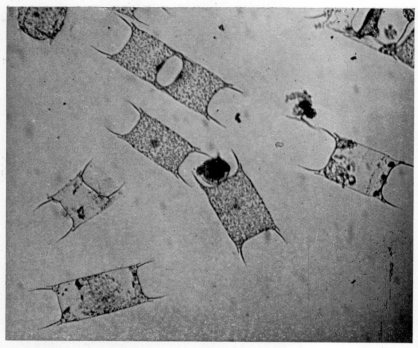

The Chinese diatom, *Biddulphia sinensis*, first appeared in British waters about sixty years ago. It had probably travelled here on ships' hulls. Now it flourishes and sometimes forms huge patches of great density in the North Sea. (*Photomicrograph* × 150)

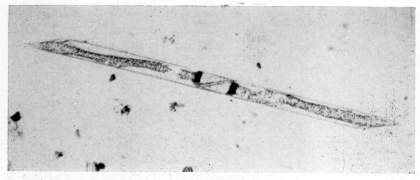

Rhizosolenia styliformis, sometimes called the glass-wool diatom, a common British species which also forms dense patches in the North Sea and some-times affects the autumn migration of herrings. (*Photomicrograph* × 150)

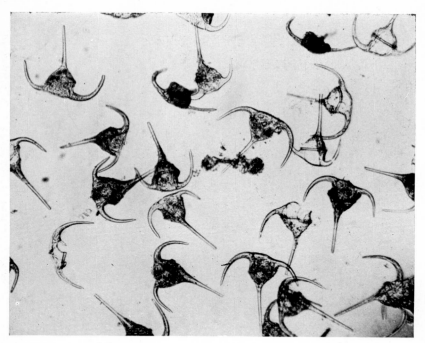

Ceratium, one of the most common of the dinoflagellates, found in most samples of sea water round our coasts. (*Photomicrograph* × 150)

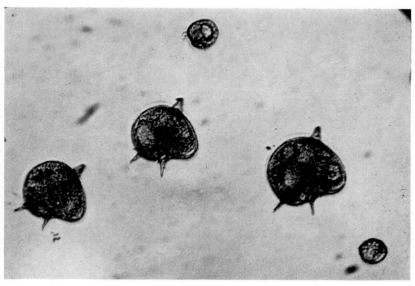

Peridinium, with its three-pointed skeleton, is another common British dinoflagellate. (*Photomicrograph* × 200)

Noctiluca—the name means 'shine-by-night'—is one of the most common and widespread of all the world's dinoflagellates. Magnified about 100 times, as in this photomicrograph, it looks rather like a transparent apple or peach complete with stalk. It is phosphorescent, and in swarms can give a magnificent display at night. It is in fact one of the chief causes of phosphorescence in temperate seas

The beautiful coiled shell of *Polystomella*, one of the most common of the Foraminifera. (*Photomicrograph* × 200)

starts life as a nauplius larva with characteristic frontal horns, and soon settles on a ship or some other under-water structure. The cement produced by cement glands at the base of the antennules fixes it firmly to its chosen site,

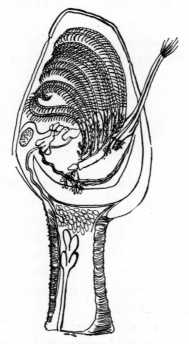

Fig. 19. The stalked or ship's barnacle, *Lepas anatifera*

usually the bottom of a ship, when most of the head degenerates. The foremost part, however, elongates to form the stalk or peduncle. The body proper consists in the main of the thorax enclosed in a carapace or mantle consisting of a fleshy investing structure strengthened by five calcified plates, two on each side and one running along the dorsal surface. Along with the thorax are the remains of the head, represented by a mouth, a pair of mandibles and a pair of maxillules. The rest consists of six well-developed pairs of biramous thoracic appendages, curled and abundantly provided with bristles. These are thrust out into the water, as are the thoracic appendages of the acorn barnacles, and by curved sweeping movements draw in suspended particles from the surrounding water.

Lepas is hermaphrodite, the ovaries lying within the peduncle, while the testes lead into an elongated penis which can penetrate into the mantle cavity of a neighbouring specimen to deposit its spermatozoa in the region of the opening of the oviduct. The fertilized eggs are retained within the mantle cavity of the females until they hatch as nauplii, when they pass out from the mantle cavity into the surrounding water.

Barnacles have always been a nuisance to shipping. They begin to settle on a ship's bottom from the moment it is launched, and within a comparatively short time their growth can appreciably slow down the vessel. Periodically ships have to be docked so that this growth can be removed. The maximum speed of a 35,000-ton battleship can be reduced through this growth by more than one knot within six months of being scraped.

Natural history in earlier times was a curious mixture of observed facts and invented myths, and even the best of the naturalists seemed quite incapable of distinguishing the one from the other. In fact, they often quoted the myths as personal observation. One of the best known of these is the story of the origin of a particular kind of goose, the barnacle or bernicle goose, from the stalked barnacles.

A fifteenth-century traveller, Sir John Mandeville, claimed to have made a special study of the barnacle goose problem, and his account of his findings makes curious reading. 'There is a small island in Lancashire called the Pile of Foulders, wherein we find broken pieces of old and bruised ships which have been cast thither by shipwrake, whereon is found a certain spume or froth which in time changeth into a certain shell like that of a muskle, but sharper pointed, wherein is a thing in form like finely woven silk. When perfectly formed the shel gapeth open, and there apeareth the legs of a bird. As it groweth bigger it all cometh forth till at length it hangeth only by the bill. In a short space of time it cometh to maturity, and falleth into the sea, where it gathereth feathers and groweth to a fowl, bigger than a mallard and lesser than a goose, which the people speak of by no other name than the tree goose, and of which a good one can be bought for three pence.' As an afterthought, presumably for the benefit of anyone who might think he was merely repeating something he had been told, he adds: 'Of that which we have seen and handled, of that do we testify.' Clearly the standards of observation in those days, even among those who professed to study nature, were not very high.

Like the acorn barnacles, *Lepas* is hermaphrodite but not self-fertilizing. In another group of stalked barnacles belonging to the genus *Scalpellum* small complemental males exist. Some species are hermaphrodite like *Lepas*, while in others there are two kinds of individuals, females of normal size, and much smaller males which live either at the entrance to or actually within the shells of the females. These males may be structurally complete or more or less degenerate, living virtually as parasites on the females. These complemental males seem to have been developed to ensure cross fertilization in solitary species where individuals would not normally be living near enough to each other to mate.

Scalpellum species live in fairly deep water attached to fixed objects, so they are not very often washed up on the shore. They possess a variable number of extra shell plates, and the peduncle is also covered with tiny shell-like scales.

The class Cirripedia contains five orders. The first of these, the order Thoracica, contains the acorn and stalked barnacles. The other important order, the Rhizocephala, consists entirely of parasites which in the adult stage are so degenerate that they bear no resemblance at all to Crustacea, or for that matter to any other group of animals. The best known of these so-called sac barnacles is *Sacculina carcini* which parasitizes the common green shore crab *Carcinus maenas*. The external evidence of infection is a yellowish structureless sac wedged between the apron and the shell, forcing the apron away from its usual position in close contact with the shell.

The appearance of this external sac is the last stage in the life of the parasite, the actual infection having occurred some time before. It, in fact, contains the eggs which are passed out into the water through a small opening at the free end to hatch as typical cirripede nauplii with the two characteristic lateral horns at the front edge. These nauplii, however, are without mouth or alimentary canal. These eventually give rise to cypris larvae, and it is these which settle on the shore crab. Each cypris larva attached itself to the base of one of the crab's setae by means of one of its antennules. The whole trunk region is now shed, leaving only the larval head. From the attached antennule a dart-like process is produced, and this penetrates the thin cuticle of the crab at the base of the seta, the remainder of the depleted body following it into the body of the crab. This structureless mass of tissue is now carried round in the crab's bloodstream until it reaches and become attached to the underside of the intestine. Rootlets now grow out in all directions, until they have penetrated to every part of the crab's body,

The Barnacles

even to the extremity of its limbs. The food materials necessary for this extensive growth are absorbed from the host's blood. At the hind end of the thorax of the crab the parasite develops a sac-like structure consisting essentially of reproductive organs. This presses upon the ventral integument of the crab just at the junction between the thorax and the abdomen or apron. When the crab next moults this sac pushes its way out of the crab's body to become the external egg sac which we have already noted, and the life cycle is ready to begin all over again. From the initial attachment of the nauplius larva to the appearance of the external sac may take as long as nine months.

Generally the host eventually dies, but before this occurs some interesting effects are produced. Before a crab moults it lays down a store of food within its body to tide it over the time when it must hide away from its enemies while its new shell is growing, and to provide the materials for the rapid growth which takes place at this time. The continual demands of the parasite, representing a heavy drain on its food resources, make it impossible for an infected crab to lay down this essential food store. In consequence it is unable to moult, and therefore cannot get rid of the acorn barnacles, tube-worms and other sedentary animals which habitually make their homes on crab shells. A crab which has survived a *Sacculina* infection for several years will thus usually be carrying about on its back a veritable museum of sedentary marine life.

Besides inhibiting moulting *Sacculina* affects the whole physiology of the crab. The reproductive organs are destroyed so that it can no longer reproduce, a condition known as parasitic castration, which leads to other abnormalities. A young infected female becomes adult in appearance more quickly than normal, while a young infected

The Barnacles

male gradually loses all male characteristics as it grows and becomes progressively more female in appearance, with smaller claws and a wider apron. The swimmerets on the apron become fringed with setae as in a typical female, where they are normally used for attaching the eggs while they develop.

Although infected crabs usually die as a result of the infection, a few survive until the parasite disappears. Reproductive organs are then regenerated when former males sometimes become hermaphrodite, producing both male and female reproductive products.

An interesting theory has been put forward to explain the effects of *Sacculina* infection. A female crab produces quantities of fatty substances for use in the yolk of the numerous eggs which it produces. These substances have a high food value and form an important part of the food absorbed by the parasite. Insufficient remains for egg production, so the crab's ovaries degenerate through disuse. Male crabs, however, normally only produce small quantities of these fatty substances, which are, however, absorbed by the parasite. This stimulates the male crab to produce them in ever greater quantities, thus changing its metabolism from typical male towards typical female, inducing corresponding structural changes in the same direction.

A very similar sac barnacle parasite called *Peltogaster paguri* is frequently found infecting hermit crabs, the external egg sac hanging down from the crab's virtually structureless abdomen. The only other member of the order which should be mentioned is *Thompsonia* which parasitizes various species of crabs, including hermit crabs, and also prawns. This is even more degenerate in the adult stage than the other two. When well established this parasite does not produce a single external sac, but many minute sacs which project between the joints of the limbs. They seem only to contain eggs, no trace of testes or spermatozoa ever having been found. The suggestion is that these eggs develop parthogenetically. They hatch out to typical cirripede nauplii, which are followed by equally typical cypris larvae which settle on the host animals.

Because in their adult stages no barnacles look at all like any other crustacea they were for a long time classed as molluscs on account of their shells. Their true relationships were revealed by one of the classic researches of the nineteenth century. In 1830 John Vaughan Thompson published a paper called *Zoological Researches and Illustrations*. Thompson was an army surgeon at that time stationed at Cork, where he was deputy inspector-general of hospitals, but his great leisure interest was marine natural history. He had discovered that crabs' eggs hatched out to larvae completely different in appearance from the adults, which only finally developed after a series of different larval stages. He then went on to discover that certain other larval stages found in the surface waters of the sea eventually developed into barnacles. But these larvae were unmistakably crustacean and so, therefore, he argued, were the adult barnacles themselves.

The other three orders of Cirripedia only require brief mention. Each contains only a few species. The order Acrothoracica is a small group of minute creatures which are unusual among the Cirripedia in that the sexes are separate. The females live fixed within hollows in mollusc shells which they themselves have excavated. Attached to them are even smaller degenerate complemental males. Darwin, who wrote a complete monograph on the Cirripedia as a result of eight years studying the group, found within the mantle cavity of a stalked barnacle *Alepas* an extremely degenerate maggot-like creature which he named *Proteolepas*, and assigned to the order Apoda. Although entirely lacking thoracic limbs, its antennules and mouth parts he recognized as being those of a cirripede. It remains to this day the sole representative of the order.

The Ascotharacica is another group of parasitic Cirripedia. Its members are regarded as more primitive than those of the other four orders because they have retained an abdomen. With this and six pairs of thoracic appendages they look much more like crustacea than any of the others. Many of them live buried right in the tissues of their hosts.

6 · Introducing the Malacostraca

We have now completed our survey of the first five classes, which might be regarded as the more primitive Crustacea, and come to the sixth and last class, the Malacostraca or higher Crustacea. This class contains greater numbers of types and a greater variety of structure than the other five classes put together, and contains all the larger Crustacea.

Despite the great variety of appearance, the fundamental structural plan remains very constant throughout the whole group. There is the usual crustacean head with its five pairs of appendages, and this is followed by a thorax of eight segments and an abdomen of six, with the exception of the members of one small sub-class, in which there is an extra abdominal segment. All the segments carry appendages. Compound eyes are always present, except in a few very degenerate forms, and they are usually carried at the end of movable stalks, which give their possessors command over the widest possible visual field. In all the adults the median eye is vestigial. Unlike any other crustacean class the Malacostraca have biramous antennules. The thoracic limbs are extremely important in their variety of functions. The endopodites are used for walking or for grasping food, the exopodites for swimming, although in some forms these may be absent, and the epipodites for respiration. The abdominal appendages are also biramous, each branch being paddle shaped. Those of the first five abdominal segments are known as pleopods, and are used in forward swimming, while the sixth pair, called uropods, turn backwards to form with the telson a tail fan which is used in rapid backward movement through the water, as we shall see later.

Typically food is collected by filtering suitable minute organisms from a stream of water set up by the maxillae and trapped by rows of setae along their inner edges.

Departure from the fundamental malacostracan plan is seen in various groups which have abandoned the typical swimming method of progression for one of walking over the sea-bed, and even in some cases of burrowing into it. In these modified forms food is no longer gathered by filtering, but is obtained in much larger particles by suitably modified thoracic limbs.

In their development many Malacostraca have dispensed with larval stages, their eggs hatching as miniature replicas of the adults. Even in those with larvae the nauplius stage is usually by-passed, the first larva being a zoaea or a schizopod.

There are five sub-classes of Malacostraca, three small ones containing comparatively primitive members of the class, and two very large ones each containing a number of orders and sub-orders. For the remainder of this chapter we shall concern ourselves with the three small groups.

Turning stones on a shore on which there is plenty of mud rich in organic matter will often reveal a tiny creature superficially resembling an enlarged *Daphnia* about half an inch long, but with a long abdomen. This is *Nebalia bipes*, the only British sea-shore representative of the sub-class Leptostraca. A large carapace not only completely covers in the thorax but the first four abdominal segments as well, its two sides being connected by a powerful adductor muscle. It is not, however, fused with any of the thoracic segments. In common with the few other members of the sub-class, and unlike any other Malacostraca, it has a seventh abdominal segment which is, however, devoid of appendages. Every other segment in the body bears its pair of appendages.

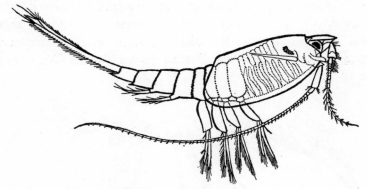

Fig. 20. *Nebalia bipes*

Nebalia's thoracic limbs are flattened biramous phyllopods each with a large epipodite which functions as a gill. Feeding is achieved by the same method as in the Branchiopoda, the thoracic limbs creating a current of water which passes down the middle groove and out between the successive pairs of limbs, the fringes of setae with which they are liberally provided filtering out the diatoms and other minute plankton organisms. These are then conveyed to the mouth in a stream of mucus. The fertilized eggs are held between the thoracic limbs of the female until they hatch. There are no larval stages, the creatures which emerge from the eggs looking like miniature replicas of their parents. The first four abdominal appendages are well developed and biramous, and are used in swimming, while the last two are small and uniramous. The front of the carapace is extended as a pointed rostrum, as in so many crustacea, but this one is unusual in that it is hinged and therefore movable.

The only other species which should be mentioned is *Nebaliopsis typica*, which lives a planktonic life at great depths in the oceans. Although many dead specimens have been brought up in plankton nets lowered to these depths, only two specimens have ever been seen alive. One of these was obtained by the Swedish research vessel *Antarctica* in 1904 and the other by the British research vessel *Discovery II* in 1954.

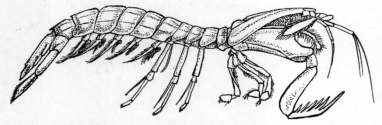

Fig. 21. The mantis shrimp, *Squilla mantis*

The best known member of the second sub-class, the Stomatopoda, is the so-called mantis shrimp, *Squilla mantis*. It has a long thin body with a small shallow carapace fused with the first three thoracic segments. The most conspicuous feature is the enormously developed second pair of thoracic limbs. The last segment of each is toothed and capable of being folded back on the preceding segment to form a formidable claw, the whole limb bearing a striking resemblance to the large claw of the praying mantis, after which the mantis shrimp is named.

Squilla lives in a burrow on the sea-bed from which its front end projects, on the watch for passing potential victims.

Introducing the Malacostraca

As soon as one comes within range it is grabbed by the claws, the teeth on the terminal section making it extremely difficult to escape. The larvae which hatch from the eggs are most extravagant in appearance, being not unlike transparent miniatures of their parents. Species of *Squilla* are found in almost every part of the world.

The third of the small sub-classes of Malacostraca is the Syncarida. These have no carapace, and are all fresh-water forms. The general structure is extremely primitive for a Malacostracan, there being little differentiation between the thorax and the abdomen. The only European species is *Bathynella*, a very degenerate species without eyes which is found in underground waters in caves, etc. A more complete form is *Anaspides*, which is found in mountain pools in Tasmania.

Having disposed of these three small sub-classes we can now devote the rest of our survey to the remaining two very large sub-classes of Malacostraca, the Peracarida and the Eucarida. The first contains the opossum shrimps, the sea slaters and woodlice, and the sand shrimps and shore hoppers. The second contains the true prawns and shrimps, the crayfishes and lobsters, the crawfishes, and the great variety of crabs.

7 · *The Peracarida*

The first of the two large malacostracan sub-classes contains five orders, the members of which vary from those completely adapted to a swimming existence to those which can only crawl along the sea-bed. All members of the group have a thoracic brood pouch in which the eggs are retained until they hatch into tiny creatures similar in appearance to the adults, there being no larval stages as there are in many other groups. Even after hatching the young usually remain in the brood pouch for protection until old enough to be able to fend for themselves. The brood pouch is formed from special plates called oostegites attached to the thoracic limbs. The carapace may fuse with some of the thoracic segments, but never with all of them.

The members of the first order, the Mysidacea, are well adapted to a swimming existence, with a general prawn-like appearance. The majority of them are marine, though a few species have become adapted to life in brackish water. Two methods of feeding are used. Movements of the maxillae and the exopodites of the thoracic limbs produce a feeding current from which minute suspended organisms are filtered, but larger food masses can be seized by the thoracic endopodites. Some of these opossum shrimps, as they are called on account of their prominent brood pouches, live on the bottom, but a few are genuinely pelagic, spend-ing their time up in the plankton.

In some species the thoracic epipodites function as gills, but in *Mysis*, the best known of the British opossum shrimps, the respiratory function has been taken over by the lining of the carapace, which is well supplied with blood channels. The epipodites are responsible for maintaining the respiratory current which sweeps through the carapace.

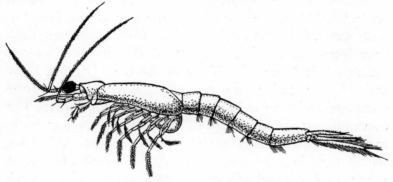

Fig. 22. *Mysis*, an opossum shrimp

The first thoracic limb in all mysids functions as a maxil-liped, while the remaining seven are typically biramous swimming appendages. In the males the abdominal appen-dages are also biramous and used in swimming, but in the females they are much reduced and sometimes absent alto-gether. The carapace, though well developed, never fuses with more than the first three thoracic segments.

A well-developed tail fan is formed from the telson and the uropods, the last pair of abdominal appendages. These uropods are unique among crustacea in that the endopodite of each carries a statocyst, such structures being absent from their more usual position in the head. The well-developed eyes are carried on stalks.

The Peracarida

Like quite a number of the smaller Crustacea the mysids are extremely transparent. In some parts of the North Sea they are so abundant that they form an important item in the diet of tiny plaice when they first settle on the sea-bed after their initial planktonic life. Some of the planktonic mysids are very beautifully coloured, and bright scarlet varieties are found in the depths of the oceans. Even those living on the bottom of the sea tend to come up into the plankton during the night.

Besides the few mysids which have become adapted to life in brackish waters there is one species which is found in fresh water. It is *Mysis relicta*, and its distribution is particularly interesting, and indeed mystifying. Its only known location is in Ennerdale Water in the Lake District. How and why a member of a typically marine group became completely adapted to life in fresh water is not known. The assumption is that at the end of the last Ice Age sea water in considerable quantities somehow flowed into this lake, which then became once more cut off from the sea. A species of *Mysis* and of a marine copepod must have come in with this water. Then as it became gradually diluted over the years by the inflow of fresh water from the surrounding hills they were able to adapt themselves gradually to the progressively lowered salt content, until eventually they gave rise to the modern fresh-water types *Mysis relicta* and *Limnocalanus macrurus*, this copepod being also of a fundamentally marine type. However they did get into the lake, there is also the intriguing problem of why over the intervening 12,000 years or so they have not managed to colonize any of the other stretches of water in the Lake District. The probable answer to this is that they have no means of travelling from one lake to another. If now they are artificially transferred they would in all probability thrive in any of the other lakes.

The Peracarida

The second order of the Peracarida is a small group known as the Cumacea. They are less active as swimmers than the mysids, tending to remain on the sea-bed, though some of them do swim up into the plankton during the night. In some species it is only the males which come up, the females remaining more or less buried in the mud below. The carapace covers only the first three or four thoracic segments, but is extended forwards at the side of the head like a pair of blinkers. Respiration is served by a large epipodite on each of the thoracic limbs. The few British species belong to the genus *Diastylis*.

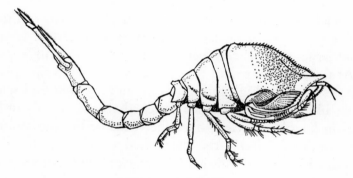

Fig. 23. *Diastylis*

The loss of swimming ability, already begun in the cumaceans, is carried a stage further in the members of the next order, the Tanaidacea. These are a small group of marine animals living on the sea-bed, the majority inhabiting burrows or tubes. A small carapace covers and fuses with the first two thoracic segments. The gills are a pair of epipodites, one on each of the first pair of thoracic appendages, which function as maxillipeds. The eyes are not stalked, and in some species they are absent altogether. The two most common British species are *Tanais cavolini* and *Apseudes talpa.* The first is a tiny creature less than a quarter of an inch long. It lives in mud tubes which it constructs in rock crevices or in grooves in wood piles below water level.

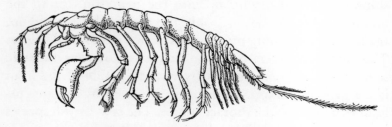

Fig. 24. *Apseudes*, which digs itself into the sea-bed

Apseudes digs itself into the sea-bed, the third pair of thoracic appendages being flattened as tiny spades. It is somewhat larger than *Tanais*, being up to half an inch in length.

At the extreme top of the shore, even beyond the splash zone reached by high spring tides, you may well find what looks like a large and rather flattened woodlouse about an inch in length, crawling over the rocks or lurking among the fronds of *Pelvetia*, the channelled wrack, which occupies this high zone. This is *Ligia oceanica*, the sea-slater, one of the largest members of the large order Isopoda. *Ligia* is in fact nocturnal, lying up in rock crevices and other cover during the day-time. At night, however, they come out in their thousands to march down the beach, where they feed on *Pelvetia* and other seaweeds. They are extremely sensitive to light, and will scuttle for cover if a torch is shone on them, and even bright moonlight will restrict the number appearing to dozens instead of thousands. Their nocturnal habits and sensitivity to light represent a defence mechanism, keeping them out of the way of the birds and crabs which feed on them.

Of all the Peracarida it is the isopods which have departed to the greatest extent from the swimming structure typical of so many crustacea. Their bodies are flattened and broad, and they have no carapace. The first thoracic segment is fused with the head, its limbs acting as maxillipeds, the remaining seven carrying pairs of uniramous walking limbs which have lost their exopodites. The abdominal segments continue the line of the thorax, so that there is no obvious point of demarcation separating them. The abdominal pleopods are biramous and flattened, and function as gills. The eyes lack stalks and the antennules are very small, though the antennae are well developed and may well be more than half the length of the body. Many members of the order are terrestrial. These are the woodlice. Many others live on the shore and are also walkers, but a few are free-swimming and found in the plankton, and some are parasites. One, the gribble, is notorious on account of its ability to bore into the wood of pier piles and harbour installations, in which activity it is second in destructive power only to the shipworm.

Several other species smaller than *Ligia* are also found on the shore. *Jaera marina* is found under stones and in crevices on almost any part of the shore. It is a tiny creature about one-sixth of an inch long, and looks very much like a miniature sea-slater, except that its colour is ash grey. *Idothea granulosa* occupies similar habitats to the other two species, and is intermediate in size between them, averaging about half an inch in length. Like them, too, it is nocturnal in its habits. It is rather more slender than the others, and therefore has a more graceful appearance, and it is also quite a good swimmer. In rock pools on the lower part of the shore, yet another species is quite common, *Eurydice pulchra*. It is about one-quarter of an inch long, semi-transparent and pale grey, and is altogether an attractive-looking creature. It is, however, carnivorous, attacking and eating other creatures smaller than itself, being an active and fast swimmer

The young of all these shore isopods hatch in the brood pouches formed by the thoracic oostegites There are no larval stages, the young closely resembling their parents, and able to fend for themselves from the moment they are released. Many shore animals represent intermediate stages in the evolution of terrestrial animals from completely aquatic marine ancestors The sea-slater *Ligia* has almost completely emancipated itself from dependence upon water, and seems therefore to be following today the same path taken by the ancestors of the terrestrial woodlice in earlier times. It is no longer dependent upon the sea for breeding or for respiration. Its only restriction is that it must remain in relatively damp places or its gills would dry up and cease to function, a restriction which also in fact applies to the woodlice, as we shall see.

As with certain crustacean groups, there are quite a number of parasites among the Isopoda. These vary from temporary parasites hardly at all modified in structure for their special mode of life, to parasites so modified and

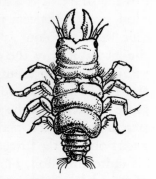

Fig. 25. *Gnathia maxillaris*, which is parasitic on fish during its larval life

degenerate in the adult state as to be unrecognizable even as Crustacea. One of the least modified is *Aega*, a fish-louse, which is somewhat heavily built but capable of leaving one host and swimming about until it can attach itself to another. Its mouth appendages are modified to pierce the host's flesh and suck up its blood. *Gnathia maxillaris* is another fish parasite, but it only lives and feeds on its host during its larval life. The adults are free-swimming, and are relatively unusual among isopods in that they regularly occur in the plankton. They exhibit a curious sexual dimorphism for which there seems to be no adequate explanation, the males having a very broad head and enormously developed mandibles which extend in front of it. The female has a head of normal size and shape, and its mandibles are reduced to vestiges. *Gnathia* is believed not to feed in the adult stage, obtaining all the food it requires for its complete life history during its parasitic larval existence.

In another group of isopod parasites there is an unusual type of hermaphroditism, in which each individual first passes through a male phase in which its structure is recognizably that of an isopod, and then changes to a female phase accompanied by varying degrees of degeneration. *Bopyrus squillarum* lives within the carapace of the prawn *Leander serratus*, where to the naked eye it appears as a greenish swelling. The male stage is less than one-tenth of an inch long, but it has normal appendages and eyes. The succeeding female stage may be up to half an inch long, but is structurally very degenerate. The whole body has become more or less oval in shape, with eyes and appendages reduced to minute vestiges, which are, however, still recognizable for what they are.

Hemioniscus balani is even more degenerate. It parasitizes acorn barnacles. Again the minute male stage shows segmentation and has seven pairs of appendages, while the female stage is completely devoid even of traces of appendages, and is really nothing more than a bag filled with eggs. *Cryptoniscus* presents a very similar picture, but is particularly interesting in that its hosts are members of the Rhizocephala or sac barnacles, so that it is what is known as a hyperparasite, that is a parasite which parasitizes another parasite.

A number of Crustacea have become adapted for boring into wood, in which they excavate burrows for protection. They are found in pier piles and wooden breakwaters, where they are capable of doing considerable damage. The most important of these is the gribble, *Limnoria lignorum*, a tiny isopod which attains a maximum length of one-fifth of an inch. Its distribution is virtually world wide, and the extent of the damage it causes is second only to that of the

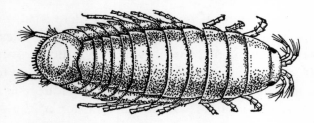

Fig. 26. The wood-boring gribble, *Limnoria lignorum*

notorious shipworm, which is a bivalve mollusc related to the mussel and the cockle. It was first discovered about 160 years ago by the famous lighthouse builder, Robert Stevenson, destroying the timbers of the Bell Rock lighthouse off the Firth of Forth.

In general structure the gribble is a typical isopod. Its first pair of thoracic appendages function as maxillipeds. The other seven pairs are uniramous, the endopodites being short powerful legs each ending in a sharp claw. With these claws the little creature is able to anchor itself firmly to the sides of its burrow. The first five abdominal appendages are typical biramous pleopods, each branch being flattened. These act as gills, and by their continuous movements they maintain an adequate respiratory current. The gribble's chief adaptation for boring is a specially modified pair of very powerful mandibles which form a rasp and file combination.

Adult gribbles are able to swim actively in the sea, and may abandon their old burrows in search of other timber. When they have found a suitable site they begin burrowing by scraping out a shallow groove along the surface of the wood, keeping to the soft part of the grain. After a short distance they then begin to go deeper, thus forming an entrance which slopes gently into the future burrow. This runs parallel with the surface and is usually less than a quarter of an inch below it, and seldom more than an inch long. At intervals, minute vertical shafts are excavated, connecting the burrow with the surface. These probably help the inhabitants to maintain a fresh respiratory current of water.

Each burrow is usually occupied by a pair of gribbles, and since the female is always in front of the male at the inner end, it seems that she must be responsible for most if not all of the work of excavating. There is an interesting difference in the behaviour of the two sexes when they are disturbed. The male backs out of the burrow, but the female clings to the wood and braces herself against the sides so effectively that only by injuring her severely can she be dislodged.

At breeding-time the female will be carrying between twenty and thirty eggs in her brood pouch. There are no larval stages, and the young gribbles which finally leave the pouch are immediately able to begin burrowing on their own account. They do not, however, leave the parent burrow, but excavate tiny burrows for themselves leading off it. Only when they are at last approaching adult size, after a number of moults, do they finally swim out into the sea to search for a new burrowing site for themselves.

Destructive though it is, the gribble has one advantage. Since it destroys the surface of whatever wood it attacks its presence is obvious, unlike that of the shipworm, which enters timbers as a microscopic larva leaving no clue as to its presence. Often it is only when the whole of the timber except the surface layer is riddled with burrows and it disintegrates that the presence of shipworm is revealed, much too late for any remedial measures to be undertaken.

As soon as a gribble population has reduced the surface layer of a piece of timber to a mass of burrows, this layer collapses, but this does not unduly inconvenience the gribbles, for they merely set about excavating homes in the next layer, which has now of course become the surface layer. Gribbles seem to prefer timber situated at about the low-tide mark. Often you will see pier or breakwater piles which have been so severely attacked at this level that they taper away almost to nothing. This is, of course, the point where they will eventually break completely.

In warmer seas than ours there is a large wood-boring isopod called *Sphaeroma*, which attains a length of half an inch. It is never present in such large numbers as the gribble, so that it is less of a menace. It can, however, live in brackish water, and so can cause substantial damage to harbour installations. Like certain terrestrial woodlice, it is capable when disturbed of rolling itself up into a ball. Another species of *Sphaeroma* found in New Zealand coastal waters is capable of excavating its burrows in sandstone and certain other soft rocks. It does considerable damage to harbour works constructed of such rocks.

The nearest relative of the terrestrial woodlice among the marine Isopoda is the common sea-slater, *Ligia*. They are indeed similar to it in structure. They have a pair of small unstalked eyes, tiny antennules but well-developed antennae. The first thoracic appendage functions as a maxilliped and the other seven are typical uniramous walking limbs each ending in a tiny claw. The first five abdominal appendages are biramous and flattened, the endopodite being thin and well supplied with blood cavities enabling it to function as a gill, while the exopodite is hard and acts as a protective cover for it. The uropods are short pointed structures, and there is no tail fan.

Although they no longer have to live in water, or even return to it to breed, the woodlice have not emancipated themselves very satisfactorily from it. Their gill surfaces must remain relatively moist to enable them to breathe, so that they are limited in their distribution to dark damp places where there is no danger of desiccation. A few of the three dozen recognized British species seem to have begun the development of a more elaborate method of respiration which might eventually make them independent of a moist atmosphere, and thus allow them to colonize drier areas at present closed to them. On some of the abdominal endopodite gills series of branching tubes run inwards, rather like the tracheal tubes of insects. The maintenance of a moist surface within these tubes would be a much easier matter than the maintenance of a moist surface on the normal flat appendage.

Like so many Crustacea, woodlice are scavengers, eating almost any plant or animal remains they come across. They will even eat each other, the victim usually being a specimen which has just moulted and therefore lacking a protective cuticle.

In their reproductive habits the woodlice are similar to other isopods. The fertilized eggs are retained within the thoracic brood pouch until they hatch, which takes about six weeks. The young resemble their parents, there being no larval stage. In a few species a curious phenomenon known as monogeny occurs, in which the members of each brood consist entirely or mainly of the same sex. No reason for this state of affairs is known.

Ecdysis in woodlice takes place in a most unusual manner. Whereas in all other crustacea the whole cuticle is shed at one time, the woodlouse moults in two stages. The first indication that it is ready to moult is that the edges of the segments turn white. This is caused by the old cuticle separating slightly from the new one which is forming underneath. A split then appears in the old cuticle between the

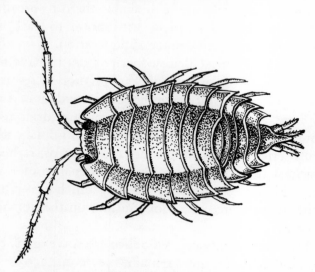

Fig. 27. *Oniscus*, one of the common woodlice

fourth and fifth thoracic segments, the animal now walking forwards, leaving the hind end of the old cuticle behind, but retaining the front end. The moulted skin is eaten, and the little creature looks most curious with its pale hind half and normal coloured front half. At this time the creature hides away, apparently realizing that without the protection of its cuticle it is very vulnerable to its enemies, and indeed even to its own kind, which would not be above eating it. Only when the new cuticle of the hind end has hardened is the front portion finally shed.

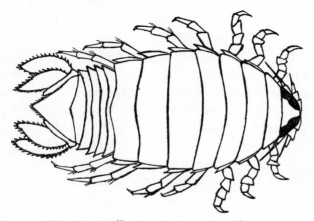

Fig. 28. *Asellus*, a common water louse

The most common species of British woodlice belong to the three genera *Oniscus*, *Porcellio* and *Armadillidium*, the latter being the kind which can roll themselves right up into a ball. Their appearance intrigued the medieval medical men, and they were often prescribed for digestive complaints both for humans and their cattle and horses. The 'pills' had to be swallowed alive! One other species should be mentioned, the blind white woodlouse *Platyarthrus hoff-mannseggi*. This is often found as a guest in ants' nests, though exactly what it is doing there no one seems to know.

Finally, among the isopods we come to those which live in fresh water. In Britain these are six closely related species of *Asellus* which are variously referred to as hog-slaters, water-slaters and water-lice. They are very common in ponds and streams where there is plenty of weed. They are active creatures, either scuttling along the bottom on their seven well-developed pairs of thoracic appendages or climbing among the plants. Their size varies, the larger species being up to an inch in length. Although the abdomen has the five pairs of flattened limbs functioning as gills, the segments themselves are all fused together. Hog-slaters are principally scavengers, feeding on all kinds of decaying organic material. They are able to stand a higher degree of pollution than most other fresh-water animals, so that their presence together with a few other species similarly adapted, is often a valuable clue that a particular stretch of water is being polluted. In one species, *Asellus aquaticus*, the males and females seem to spend the winter in pairs, the male habitually carrying the female under him. This does not occur in the very similar *Asellus meridianus*, in which for some unexplained reason there are many more males than females. These two are the most common and widespread species.

The other large order of Peracarida is the Amphipoda. Like the Isopoda these too are compressed, but from side to side instead of from above. The characteristic members of the group are the various species of *Gammarus*, the sand- and fresh-water shrimps. There is no carapace, but the first thoracic segment is fused with the head, its appendages functioning as maxillipeds. The other thoracic limbs, like those of the Isopoda, have no exopodites. The first two pairs end in tiny prehensile claws, which help the maxillipeds in conveying food to the mouth. The other five pairs are used by the animal to drag itself along when it is lying on its side. The six abdominal appendages are biramous and consist of two distinct sets. The first three are many jointed and

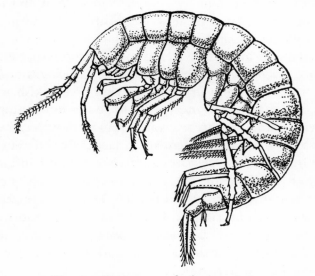

Fig. 29. *Gammarus*, a freshwater shrimp

are used for swimming, and also for directing the respiratory current of water over the gills. The last three are directed backwards, and are used by many of the amphipods to give the ground a sharp kick and send them jumping up into the air. When normally at rest the body is arched into a curve, straightening only when the animal decides to swim.

The various species of *Gammarus* form an interesting series of closely related creatures adapted to live in waters of varying salinities. Two species are commonly found under stones and hiding among the seaweeds on the shore. These are *Gammarus marinus* and *Gammarus locusta*. They feed on dead organic matter, as do so many of the Amphipoda, and such scavengers are very valuable in preventing the accumulation of decaying material whose smell would make the shore unbearable. Neither species could live in the brackish waters of estuaries. Equally abundant in streams and rivers are the closely related fresh-water shrimps, the most common of which is *Gammarus pulex*, which is just as incapable of surviving in brackish water as the two shore species. But there are *Gammarus* species in estuaries. *Gammarus zaddachi* is extremely common in most stretches of brackish water, which of course, means most estuaries, but is quite incapable of survival either in pure sea water or in fresh water. Recent research has shown that there are in fact three different subspecies of *zaddachi*. *Gammarus zaddachi salinus* is confined to the lower parts of estuaries, where the proportion of salt is greater than it is in the higher reaches. Here it is replaced by *Gammarus zaddachi zaddachi*. In Scotland a third sub-species has been recognized, *Gammarus zaddachi oceanicus*, which replaces and occupies the same esturarine zone as the subspecies *salinus* farther south.

One other species of *Gammarus* should be mentioned, *Gammarus tigrinus*, which is found in brine pools in Cheshire, where of course the salt content is very much greater than it is in the sea or on the shore.

On the shore *Gammarus* species occur fairly low down, so that they are true littoral species, being covered by each tide and actively swimming. Even more abundant on almost all shores are the sand-hoppers and shore-hoppers, *Talitrus saltator* and *Orchestria gammarellus*, but they occur so far up the shore that they are only submerged by the incoming tide accidentally. Both are very similar in structure and appearance to *Gammarus*.

At the extreme high-tide mark on any sandy shore there

is an accumulation of seaweed and other deposited debris. If this is turned over, and particularly if the sand beneath it is disturbed, there will almost certainly be a cloud of tiny creatures jumping into the air. These are the sand-hoppers, which can appear in fantastic numbers. *Talitrus saltator* is a nocturnal animal, and each morning it burrows into the sand beneath the debris at the high-tide mark. Unless disturbed it will remain there until nightfall, when it will come out to feed on whatever organic debris it can find. If the tide is out it will travel far down the shore in search of plant and animal remains, always returning before the incoming tide, and ready to bury itself before daylight reappears. *Talitrus* must be regarded as one of those shore animals, like *Ligia*, which has almost emancipated itself from dependence on the sea, and is on the way to becoming a completely terrestrial creature. Submergence for any length of time in sea water is said to be fatal to it, but on the other hand it still seems to need the presence of salt in the sand in which it lives.

If stones are turned or weed debris disturbed on a rocky shore the very similar shore-hopper, *Orchestria gammarellus*, appears in equally large numbers. Its habits are very similar to those of *Talitrus*. Both species are capable of jumping for a distance of several feet by straightening their bodies and using the last three pairs of backwardly directed abdominal appendages.

Although the sand-shrimps and the sand- and shore-hoppers are the most abundant shore amphipods, they are by no means the only ones. On the lower parts of the shore you may find *Amphithoe rubricata*, similar in build to the other kinds but rather smaller. It is, however, more difficult to locate, because besides living under boulders or heavy weed cover it hides away when the tide is out in a tubular nest made of fragments of seaweed held together by strong threads which are produced by certain special glands on its legs.

Several other genera of amphipods live buried in wet sand on the lower parts of the shore, the most common being *Bathyporeia, Urothoe* and *Haustorius*. All are capable of swimming but all spend much of their time buried just below the surface of the sand. The first two swim normally, but *Haustorius* always swims upside down. All three feed on debris which they find in the sand in which they burrow, so that there is no necessity for them to come out into the water at every tide. *Bathyporeia*, for example, comes out only at night, and is found only in large numbers at fortnightly intervals. It is thought that these mass appearances may coincide with mating or with the release of their young into the water. The eggs are known to take about a fortnight to develop, so it is possible that mating takes place at one appearance and liberation of the young at the next.

Corophium volutator is a similar burrowing species, but its chosen habitat is mud or muddy sand. Although the little creatures are only about one-third of an inch long, they construct burrows in mud banks up to five inches deep. These are strengthened by a sticky secretion produced by glands on the second pair of thoracic appendages. Periodically they emerge from their burrows to crawl over the mud, feeding on organic particles which they pick up from the surface. They are able to live in brackish as well as salt water, and are therefore common in muddy estuaries.

Although nothing like so numerous as the copepods, the amphipods are nevertheless quite well represented in the plankton. A notable feature of these planktonic amphipods is that they all have enormous eyes. One of the most common in British waters is *Themisto gracilipes*. In some years this occurs in such huge numbers off the east coast of Scotland and northern England that it may form the main item in the diet of herring caught during the Shields summer fishery. The closely related *Hyperia galba* is one of a small group of marine animals which habitually take advantage of the shelter afforded by the umbrellas of the larger jellyfish. Here they are able to take a share of their protectors' planktonic food, and gain protection from their enemies, which would not dare to risk an encounter with the stinging tentacles of the jellyfish.

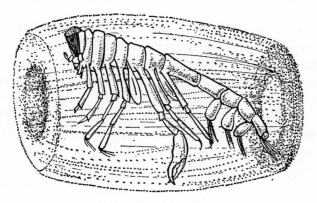

Fig. 30. *Phronima sedentaria*

The most picturesque of all these planktonic amphipods is *Phronima*, which is common in the Mediterranean and the subtropical Atlantic, but also comes into our seas on occasion. It has evolved a novel method of protection. In the plankton there are large numbers of creatures called salps, small animals which live within a transparent barrel-shaped gelatinous shell or tunic, open at both ends, which they themselves have produced. *Phronima* attacks such a salp, eats the contained animal and thus takes over its barrel-shaped tunic as its home. In its commandeered home it can feed and

G   **97** produce its young. In plankton samples a female has been seen pushing in front of it a barrel full of young.

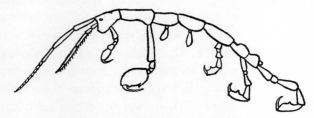

Fig. 31. The ghost or skeleton shrimp, *Caprella aequilibra*

One of the most fascinating of all crustacea is the tiny ghost or skeleton shrimp, *Caprella aequilibra*. It is extremely thin, transparent and elongated, its common names giving a very apt description of its appearance. It neither swims nor walks, but is adapted to what has been described as an arboreal life, spending its time in rock pools, climbing among the branches of the small algae which grow there. Because of its transparency and its habit of remaining completely still for long periods in a more or less upright position, so that it resembles one of the branches of the weed, it is a very difficult animal to locate, though it is quite common and widely distributed.

The first two thoracic segments are fused with the head, while the third bears a pair of strong claws. The fourth and fifth segments lack appendages altogether, but they each carry a pair of flattened structures which function as oostegites in the female. The last three thoracic segments each carries a pair of well-developed hooked appendages, by means of which the tiny creature anchors itself firmly when it raises the rest of its body in the air. In this position the large appendages of the third thoracic segment are held out ready to grab at any tiny creature which swims close enough to be captured. In this watching position the skeleton shrimp is strongly reminiscent of the praying mantis when it is similarly poised waiting for unsuspecting victims.

In its specialized method of existence an abdomen would possibly be a hindrance. It is in fact reduced to a tiny vestigial stump attached to the last thoracic segment. When the skeleton shrimp wants to, it can move quite rapidly, either swinging from branch to branch or, on the ground, by a looping movement similar to that of a looping caterpillar. Several different species of *Caprella* occur on our shores.

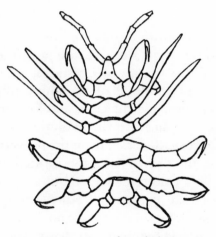

Fig. 32. *Cyamus*, the whale-louse

Another caprellid has become adapted to an entirely different mode of life. It is *Cyamus*, the whale-louse, whose body is short and wide. As its name suggests it is an external parasite of whales.

8 · *Prawns, Shrimps, Lobsters and their Allies*

Although they constitute only one of the five sub-classes of the Malacostraca, the Eucarida are nevertheless the most important of all the groups of Crustacea, containing all the larger species and all those of economic importance, the shrimps and prawns, and the crabs and lobsters. Within the sub-class, too, we can trace the evolution of the complete crawling crustacean, the crab, from the powerful swimming Crustacea like the prawns and the lobsters. As Gosse observed, the edible crab can swim about as well as a stone of the same size! One structural feature distinguishes all the Eucarida from any other crustacean. The carapace fuses with all the thoracic segments, so that if you find a crustacean, and can raise the carapace from the hind end and separate it from any of the thoracic segments, you are not dealing with a eucaridan.

There are two orders within the sub-class. The first, the order Euphausiacea, is a small group of planktonic shrimp-like creatures with almost worldwide distribution. Certain species are of great importance in the economy of the seas because they form the principal item in the diet of the large whalebone whales, and are thus comparable with the copepod *Calanus finmarchicus*, which, as we have already seen, is the principal item in the diet of the herring.

The second order, the Decapoda, contains a great variety of Crustacea, all the prawns, shrimps, lobsters and crabs, comprising a very large number of species some of which are found in the seas, on the shores, and even on land near the sea, in almost every part of the world. The name of the order refers to the fact that the last five of the invariable eight thoracic segments bears a pair of walking limbs. The first, and sometimes the second pair also, may in fact no longer be used for walking, but instead may be provided with pincers for use in defence and in obtaining food. In this chapter we shall confine our attention to the true swimming Eucarida, the euphausids, and the prawns, shrimps and lobsters and their relatives. The great variety of crab life will require two additional chapters for their adequate consideration.

At first glance the euphausiaceans look very similar to the mysids. The carapace test will, however, distinguish them, and there are other important differences. The euphausiaceans have no statocysts on their uropods, and the inner lining of the carapace does not act as a respiratory organ. Instead very efficient feathery gills well supplied with blood capillaries are borne on all eight pairs of thoracic appendages, none of which function as maxillipeds. These are all biramous, as are the six pairs of abdominal appendages. The first five pairs of these are paddle-like swimmerets, while the sixth pair, the uropods, form with the telson a conspicuous tail fan.

The largest and most important of the European euphausiaceans is *Meganyctiphanes norvegica*, which occurs in some of the deep water Scottish lochs, such as Loch Fyne, as well as in the open seas almost everywhere in the North Atlantic.

Prawns, Shrimps, Lobsters and their Allies

Like all the euphausiaceans it is almost transparent, but with a pair of enormous black eyes. The West Coast Scottish fishermen call it suil dhu, which means 'black eye'. To the Norwegian whalers it is the northern krill, and it forms the

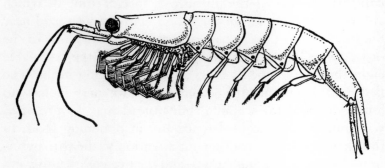

Fig. 33. *Meganyctiphanes norvegica*, the northern krill

main item in the diet of all the northern whalebone whales. It is also quite an important item in the diet of the herring at certain times of the year. Full grown specimens measure up to 1½ inches in length. Certain other species occur in British waters, notably *Nyctiphanes couchi*, particularly common in the North Sea and in the English Channel, and *Thysanoessa rachii*, common in the inshore water of the west coast of Scotland.

In the Antarctic regions there are other equally important euphausiaceans, which form the main item in the diet of the southern whalebone whales. The most important of them all is *Euphausia superba*, which grows to about two inches in length, and like *Meganyctiphanes norvegica* occurs in immense shoals containing vast numbers of individuals. These are the southern krill.

Vertical migration, and its possible use in helping to maintain a drifting planktonic animal in the same geographical position has already been mentioned. It is particularly well

Prawns, Shrimps, Lobsters and their Allies

seen in these southern euphausiacean species. In Antarctic regions the upper 100 yards or so of very cold water flows northwards, while beneath it a similar current of warmer water flows southwards towards the ice cap. At least some of the Antarctic euphausiaceans come into the upper layer during the night, when they will be carried steadily north-wards. By daylight, however, they have sunk down into the warmer southward current, in which they travel virtually the same distance in the opposite direction, the net result of their travels being to keep them more or less in the same geographical position.

In their reproductive habits the euphausiaceans are very different from the mysids. The eggs are fertilized internally by spermatozoa which are transferred to the female by the male in spermatophores similar to but larger than those we have already seen in the Copepoda. To enable it to carry out this transference the first abdominal appendages of the male are much modified as 'fingers' to insert the spermatophores. There is no brood pouch, the eggs being shed into the water, where they hatch as nauplii.

One particularly interesting feature of the euphausiaceans is their well-developed set of luminous organs. These can be seen as red spots, one on each of the eye-stalks, one on the bases of each of the second and seventh pairs of thoracic limbs, and one on each side of each of the first four pairs of abdominal segments. These light-producing organs or photophores each consists of a layer of cells capable of pro-ducing flashes of light, backed by a reflecting layer and with a lens in front. Six specimens of *Meganyctiphanes norvegica* in a jar and producing their maximum light flashes have been recorded as producing enough light to enable news-print to be read.

Quite a number of types of marine animals are able to

produce this living light, and it is a phenomenon reasonably common among certain Crustacea, especially deep-sea prawns. A good deal is now known about this living light and how it is produced, but so far no really satisfactory explanation as to its purpose has been put forward, at least for the majority of species which produce it. In certain fishes the beam of phosphorescent light does seem to be a means of producing sufficient light to enable them to detect and catch their prey, but the phosphorescence of bacteria, which causes the fish on the larder slab to glow when you see it in the dark, or the phosphorescence of the flagellates which was mentioned in an earlier chapter, do not seem to have any conceivable advantage for the organisms themselves. In most of the Crustacea which possess photophores, and in many other animals too, these project their light away from the direction in which the eyes are facing, thus making it seem unlikely that their use can be to illuminate possible prey.

Phosphorescence is sometimes known as cold light. All man-made sources of light dissipate much of the energy they use as heat, only the remainder being available for the production of light. But in phosphorescence 99 per cent of the energy is converted into light, only 1 per cent being wasted as heat. If we could devise means of lighting our buildings and streets as efficiently, our electricity and gas bills would be considerably reduced.

The first of the six decapod sub-orders comprises a small group of primitive prawns, the Penaeidea. None of these occur in British waters, and the only one we are likely to meet is the Mediterranean prawn *Penaeus*, which now occurs quite commonly in restaurants and high-class snack counters. Their chief interest lies in the fact that they are the only Decapoda to hatch as nauplii, and thus undergo a com-

plete crustacean development. The members of all the other
five orders hatch as more advanced larvae, as we shall see.

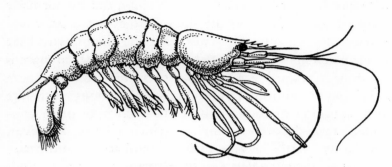

Fig. 34. Common prawn, *Leander serratus*

The second decapod sub-order is the very important
group of Caridea, which includes all the true prawns and
shrimps. There are several British prawns, but the largest
and most important commercially is *Leander serratus*. In life
it is almost transparent, and ideally constructed for an active
swimming life. The first two of the five pairs of thoracic
appendages end in tiny pincers, and are used to grasp food,
the last three pairs being well developed as walking limbs,
and are used by the prawn to walk along the bottom of the
rock pool or the sea-bed. The abdomen is well developed,
and has five pairs of biramous pleopods which are used for
gentle forward swimming. Setae on the inner edges of each
pair enable them to be locked together for greater swimming efficiency. The last pair of abdominal appendages are
well-developed uropods, which with the telson, form a
wide tail fan. When the creature is alarmed this can be
turned forward beneath the body and so drive it rapidly
backwards though the water.

As an active animal its sense organs are well developed.
The antennules each have three branches which spread out

to search the environment in front of and above the head, the two long branches being as long as the whole body. The antennae are half as long again as the body, and are normally trailed backwards along the sides. The eyes are large and carried on long movable stalks, enabling the prawn to see in virtually any direction. Between the eyes the carapace is continued forward as a prominent serrated rostrum.

During the summer months prawns of various species are very common in rock pools, a fair-sized pool often containing several dozen specimens, which are not, however, easy to see, partly because of their transparency and partly because of their tendency to hide away among the fronds of the weeds growing round the edges of the pool. In the autumn, as the temperature begins to fall, the prawns forsake their pools and move out to sea, where they will remain in shallow water until the spring.

Adult crabs and lobsters moult only once a year, but during the summer prawns do so every two or three weeks. One of the moults in the female represents a breeding moult, and she emerges from it with long setae growing on her swimmerets. Before her new shell hardens mating takes place, and she lays her eggs. These are attached to the hairs on the swimmerets by means of a cement produced by special glands on the last pair. A female prawn in berry, as she is described when she is carrying fertilized eggs, may be carrying as many as 2,000 of them. They do not hatch as nauplius larvae, but as a special type of larva called a zoea, which is found only among the Decapoda, and will be described in the chapter on the crabs. Soon after her eggs have hatched the female prawn moults again and loses the hairs which constituted her breeding-dress. Sometimes a prawn may spawn twice during one season.

Besides *Leander serratus* we have several other British

prawns. Very similar in appearance, but seldom exceeding two inches in length, is the closely related *Leander squilla*, which is more common on rocky shores than the larger species. This and the other smaller species of prawn are often sold by the fishmonger as 'pink shrimps', a misnomer because all shrimps when boiled are brown. Another quite common species is *Pandalus montagui*, known variously as the Aesop prawn and, in Lancashire, as the Fleetwood prawn.

One of the most interesting of all the British Crustacea is the little chameleon or humped prawn, *Hippolyte varians*, on account of its remarkable ability to change colour so as to blend with its surroundings. The colouring of an animal may be a very important factor in protecting it from its enemies. Many animals have a colour pattern which blends with their normal surroundings, so that they are camouflaged. Sometimes the structure of the animal is also modified to reinforce the effect of the protective coloration, as is the case with the well-known stick insect, which is not only coloured like the twigs of the plant on which it lives, but even has the shape of a twig.

Certain animals have so perfected the art of colour and pattern camouflage that they are able to adjust the pattern of their colouring so as to match any particular colour scheme in which they may find themselves. The Crustacea are particularly gifted in this direction, both the shrimp and the prawn being able to adjust their colour to blend with their background. Because of its outstanding ability in this direction, the chameleon prawn is very difficult to find, but it is in fact quite common in rock pools, where it spends most of its time clinging to the weeds.

Young chameleon prawns are colourless when they settle from the plankton, but within a short time they have developed a body colour to match that of the weed on which they find themselves. If a red specimen on a red weed in an aquarium tank is transferred to another tank in which the weeds are green, it first seems to travel around as though searching for a red weed. When none can be found it eventually settles on a green weed and gradually changes its own colour from red to green. These colour changes are slow, and it will be several days before the prawn finally matches the colouring of its surroundings completely.

The method by which the chameleon prawn and other Crustacea achieve their changes of colour has been very carefully investigated. All over the surface there are large numbers of pigment cells of special shape, called chromatophores. Each consists of a small body from which processes radiate in all directions. In every chromatophore there are three pigments, a yellow, a red and a blue, each of which can spread through the cell processes or be withdrawn as required. When a specimen adopts a red weed the red pigment flows through the cell while the blue and yellow are retained within its body. If it is now placed on a green weed the blue and yellow pigments flow out and the red is withdrawn. At night, irrespective of its day-time colouring, the chameleon prawn becomes blue, the other pigments being withdrawn.

These colour changes in the Crustacea are under the control of hormones, substances produced in special glands called ductless glands, because their products diffuse out into the blood instead of being carried away by a special duct. They pass into the blood when required, and so reach the part of the body which they are designed to control. The hormones which control the colour changes in Crustacea are produced in glands in the eye-stalks. It is thought that secretion of the hormones is controlled by the colour of the light from the surroundings, acting either directly on the glands or indirectly through the eyes.

Many animals belonging to other groups have a similar hormone mechanism controlling their colour changes. Good examples are the chameleon and the various flatfish, such as the plaice, the turbot and the sole. These latter are able to produce a pattern on their upper surface which blends with the pattern of the ground over which they are swimming. Since the same side is always uppermost, this is the only side needing pigment cells, which explains why flatfish are coloured on one side only, the lower side being white.

Hormone actions in animals are characteristically slow, and all these colour changes take place gradually. Some animals, notably the octopus, have a much quicker method of colour change, in which the chromatophores are under the direct control of the nervous system. For this reason it is able to change colour almost instantaneously.

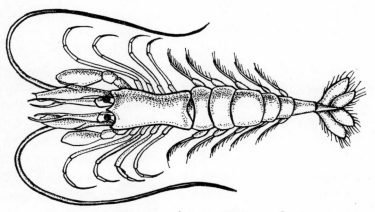

Fig. 35. Common shrimp, *Crangon vulgaris*

In their habits and in their structure shrimps are quite different from prawns, and although we have several distinct prawn species, as we have just seen, there is only one British species of shrimp, *Crangon vulgaris*. You will not find shrimps in rock pools because they are sand-burrowing animals, which live buried during the day-time just beneath the surface of the sand in the shallow offshore waters, coming out on to the surface to feed at night. Compared with the prawn, the body of the shrimp is noticeably flattened from above, and seems correspondingly to spread out more to the sides, so that the limbs of the right and left sides are more widely separated. One of the characteristic features of the prawn's external appearance is the prominent serrated rostrum. This is absent in the shrimp.

In the shrimp only the first pair of thoracic legs carry pincers, and these are quite different from the prawn's two pairs of pincers. The end segment of each of the first pair of legs is a very stout structure which can be bent back on to the second segment, the two acting together as the jaws of the pincers. When it does come out of the sand, the shrimp is not as graceful as the prawn in its movements. It does not usually swim, although it can do so if pressed, but walks about on the sea-bed, using only its last two pairs of thoracic legs. The long third pair seem to act as a third pair of feelers, and are used along with the antennules and antennae to investigate any objects encountered. With their powerful pair of pincers the shrimps are able to deal with larger objects than the prawns, and will in fact eat almost anything that presents itself, including various small algae, small crustaceans, larvae of all kinds and very small fishes. They have even been seen eating worms bigger than themselves.

If you can get hold of a shrimp and place it in a sandy pool, or in a tank with sand on the bottom, you will be able to see how it burrows, and will also realize how its structure is adapted to its mode of life. As soon as it drops on to the sand both legs and swimmerets start moving. The legs beat backwards and outwards so that they scoop out the sand from beneath the thorax, pushing it to the sides. At the same time the swimmerets move rapidly backwards and forwards causing a current of water which sweeps out the sand from beneath the abdomen. In a very short time a shallow depression is formed, and the shrimp stops beating with its limbs and swimmerets and sinks down into it. The deepening of this depression is then taken over by the cara-pace, the sides of which, forming the covers to the gills, are moved outward and inwards, forcing water out of the gill chambers. This sends the sand from the bottom of the depres-sion upwards, and so the shrimp sinks deeper. When at last the top of the body is sunk below the level of the sand, the feelers are used to sweep sand from the sides over the top, so finally covering the shrimp completely. Except for the end sections left above the sand to detect any suitable food which may be swept past, the antennae are finally buried too.

Most animals which live in the sea are unable to survive in fresh water, just as typical fresh-water species will soon die if placed in sea water. This is because each type is ad-justed to the particular kind of water in which it normally lives. A marine animal placed in fresh water will absorb water into its body, thus disturbing the whole balance of its body fluids, and so leading to its death. A fresh-water species in sea water loses water from its body with equally serious effects. A few animals, however, have acquired greater control over the composition of their body fluids, and are therefore able to live in waters of varying composition. Many of these animals are typically found in estuaries, where the composition of the mixed waters of the river and the sea is liable to considerable fluctuation. Others are true marine animals which are also able to travel into estuaries and live there indefinitely.

The shrimp is one of those animals able to adjust itself to the low salinity of estuaries as well as to the fully saline conditions in the sea. In the summer shrimps are often extremely abundant in the brackish water of estuaries. They seem less able to endure low salinity in the winter, however, so that those individuals which have lived in estuaries during summer months usually migrate down to the open sea in the late autumn. Berried females, too, always travel out to sea before their broods hatch.

Even if disturbed out of the sand in shallow water the shrimp is still not easy to detect provided it remains still. Although it may be found in any kind of sand from pure yellow sand to very dark muddy sand, its chromatophores produce a perfect colour match. When boiled, the shrimp becomes brown. It is in fact known to commerce as the brown shrimp, to distinguish it from the pink shrimp, which as we have already seen is really a small prawn.

Shrimping forms quite an important local industry in certain parts of the country, notably in Morecambe Bay in Lancashire, the Essex and Kent coasts, and the shores of the Bristol Channel. Several methods of catching shrimps are adopted in various places, but they nearly all depend upon the same principle. If the first inch or so of the sand in which they are living is disturbed they will come up to the surface. The amateur shrimper uses a net which has a straight bar forming its front edge. This is pushed through the upper layer of sand and so disturbs the shrimps, many of which will be swept into the capacious net which trails behind the bar.

This hand net is in effect a simple trawl. Larger shrimping trawls are used commercially, drawn by small inshore fishing-vessels, while in some places similar trawls are drawn along the sea-bed in shallow water by horse-drawn carts. In the Bristol Channel the traditional method of catching shrimps is by nets which are permanently fixed so that the water of the outgoing tide passes through them. Any shrimps present in the water are thus caught and held in the nets until they can be examined after the tide has receded beyond them. Often there will be plenty of prawns swimming just above the grounds in which the shrimps lie buried, and these are also caught by the shrimping-trawls. Similar trawls hauled across rocky ground where there are no shrimps will produce a haul of various prawn species.

The third decapod sub-order, the Astacura, contains the lobsters and the fresh-water crayfishes. The most important species is the common lobster, *Homarus vulgaris*, which is economically the most valuable of all the Crustacea. It is a typical swimming decapod, and is large enough to show all the principal features of the order quite clearly. The antennules are biramous, with two short branches, and are situated on either side of the rostrum. The antennae are also biramous, but the exopodite is so short as to be easily overlooked compared with the extremely long many-jointed endopodite, which when swept backwards reaches practically to the end of the body. There are the usual mouth parts consisting of paired mandibles, maxillules and maxillae, as well as three pairs of maxillipeds representing the appendages of the first three thoracic segments.

The five remaining pairs of thoracic segments are the walking limbs. The first pair of these are the chelipeds, and end in large pincers or chelae. These are larger in males than in females, and in both sexes the two differ in structure. One, usually the left, is longer than the other, and the inner edges of the chelae are furnished with a few large teeth. The other cheliped has a larger number of much smaller teeth.

The pincers with the few large teeth are the ones used mainly in combat. Lobsters are pugnacious creatures, always liable to start fighting when they meet, and often losing one or both of their chelipeds in the process. As we shall see later, in dealing with crabs, loss of limbs by decapods is not an unusual occurrence, and such limbs as are lost will grow again and eventually reach full size after two or three moults. The second and third pairs of thoracic walking-limbs also bear tiny pincers while the last two pairs are pointed.

All six pairs of abdominal appendages are represented. The first pair are small and apparently functionless in the female lobster, but in the male they are modified to form sperm-carrying ducts. The next four pairs are typical biramous swimmerets, while the last pair, the uropods, are well developed, and form with the telson the tail fan. This is much wider and better developed in the female than in the male.

Lobsters are common and widespread in shallow water on all coasts where there is any rock cover. Their normal colour is bluish black, though pale red specimens are sometimes caught. The normal blue specimens only become red when they are boiled. They are voracious feeders, eating almost anything they come across, and they are not fussy about their meat being fresh.

Lobster- and crab-fishing occurs all around our coasts wherever there are off-shore rocks, the method of catching them being by means of baited lobster-pots or creels, the latter being the Scottish version of the southern lobster-pot. Fish which is no longer fresh forms the best bait, enticing the lobsters to enter the pots during the night when they come out of their holes in the rocks to feed. They are usually taken up first thing in the morning, being rebaited and sunk again as soon as any crabs and lobsters found in them have been removed. When they are brought back to harbour lobsters are often stored alive for a few days in floating boxes until they are wanted. Before being put in, however, their claws are tied with string to prevent them fighting and damaging one another.

The chief enemy of crabs and lobsters is the octopus, which goes out hunting for them at night. As it swims through the water it descends like a cloud over any unfortunate crab it encounters. Even when hiding in its lair during the day-time, it remains on the alert for any unsuspecting crab which may happen to pass, flicking out one of its arms to touch the crab lightly as soon as it comes within reach. Then a curious thing happens. The crab raises itself on its legs and holds up its claws in a typical defensive attitude, as though it is going to attack the octopus's arm. But that is apparently as far as its defensive instincts take it, for it appears to be in some way hypnotized by the octopus, which without further trouble is able to drag it in and tuck it away in the folds of its arm webs.

The captured crab may be kept alive for some time while others are collected. One octopus was observed to collect no fewer than seventeen crabs before finally settling down to its meal. To get at the crab meat it pulls off the claws and legs, and then uses the flexible tips of its arms to extract the meat and pass it into its mouth. An octopus lair can sometimes be discovered by the heap of empty crab-shells lying around the entrance.

Lobsters are more difficult for the octopus to catch than crabs, because they show no signs of being afraid of it. The danger, of course, is the lobster's claws, and the first aim of the octopus is to get a grip on these. Once it has succeeded the lobster is vanquished, but a prolonged battle of wits may occur before a really big lobster is overpowered. A story is told of an aquarium octopus which managed to escape from its own tank and enter a neighbouring tank of lobsters. For hours a battle ensued between the octopus and a large lobster, with honours even at the end of the day when the spectators withdrew. By the next morning, however, the keepers arrived to find the octopus sleeping peacefully, surrounded by the empty shells not only of its previous day's opponent, but of those of all the other occupants of the tank as well.

Because of its partiality for crabs and lobsters, the octopus can be a menace to the in-shore fishermen. When octopuses are plentiful the fishermen all too frequently haul up a lobster-pot only to find it occupied by an octopus surrounded by the empty shells of what should have been a good catch of lobsters. Around the Channel Islands and off the north-west coast of France the octopus is usually fairly common during the summer. Its numbers vary considerably, however, and sometimes reach plague proportions. In 1899 and 1900 the crab and lobster fisheries in these areas were completely ruined by an octopus plague, which extended to our own south-western shores in the latter year.

Quite closely related to the common lobster, but smaller, is the Norway lobster, *Nephrops norvegicus*. Its general ground colour is orange with red markings, and it lives on muddy ground in fairly deep water, usually between 30 and 60 fathoms, and is brought up in the trawls. It is widespread in the North Sea, and used to be caught in large numbers in the Irish Sea, when it was also known as the Dublin Bay prawn. Today it is best known as the scampi which has become so popular in hotels and restaurants. Unlike the lobster it cannot be kept alive and must be boiled as soon as it is caught. Only the tails are of any use, so the rest of the animal is thrown away.

Prawns, Shrimps, Lobsters and their Allies

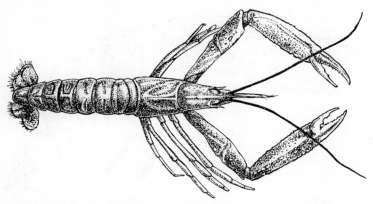

Fig. 36. The Norway lobster or Dublin Bay prawn, *Nephrops norvegicus*, better known today as scampi

The only other member of the Astacura which has any interest for us is the fresh-water crayfish, *Astacus fluviatilis*. In structure it is virtually identical with the common lobster, but much smaller. It averages about four inches in length, which makes it the largest British fresh-water invertebrate. It can only live in well-oxygenated water in which there is plenty of lime or chalk, so it is found only in fast-moving streams in chalk and limestone districts. Here, however, it may be extremely abundant. Like so many of the larger Crustacea it is a nocturnal creature, lying up during the day-time in burrows in the river bank or under large stones, coming out at night to feed. It is carnivorous, eating almost any kind of animal material which comes its way, including water snails, aquatic larvae of insects, and even tadpoles.

Mating takes place in the late autumn, and begins with the male turning the female over on its back and then shedding his seminal fluid over her abdomen. It is a sticky liquid, and adheres to the hairs on the swimmerets. The female now retires to her burrow, where she lays her hun-

117

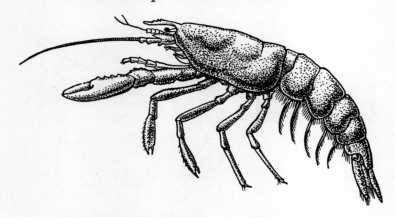

Fig. 37. The fresh water crayfish, *Astacus fluviatilis*

dred or so eggs. These she attaches to the swimmeret hairs, and in this way they come into contact with the seminal fluid and are fertilized. She carries them about with her right through the winter, and in the spring they finally hatch as tiny crayfish. Usually they will remain attached to her swimmerets until they have grown somewhat before breaking away to lead their own lives. This direct production of young without intermediate larval stages represents an adaptation to life in rivers. Free-swimming larvae such as are produced by the vast majority of marine Crustacea would be swept out to sea.

In some districts where they were once very common, the fresh-water crayfish are becoming rare. Two suggestions have been put forward to account for this, one that it has been caused by a protozoan disease, and the other that drainage from tarred roads running into the streams has killed them. This latter may well be a cause, because it is known that they are very susceptible to tar in the water in which they are living.

Crayfish are regarded as a delicacy. They are usually

caught by tying a piece of meat to the middle of a hoop net
and lowering it into the river at night. After being left for a
time it is then drawn up, when the crayfish are found firmly
fixed to the bait by their claws. As with scampi, the tails or
abdomens are the only part of the body large enough to be
worth bothering about.

The last British representative of the swimming Decapoda
is the crawfish or rock lobster, *Palinurus vulgaris*. The chief
differences between the crawfish and the lobster are that the
crawfish lacks any pincers on any of its thoracic legs, and its
carapace is very spiny. It lives generally in rather deeper
water than the lobster, but does live on rocky ground,
hiding away during the day-time in suitable rock clefts.

The crawfish is more popular on the Continent than it is
here. It is in fact the true French *langouste*. Cornish and Devon
fishermen sometimes exchange them with French fishermen
for lobsters.

9 · *The Hermit Crabs and their Relatives*

The Eucarida we met in the last chapter were all fundamentally swimming types, having a well-developed and powerful abdomen which could be used for rapid backward movement through the water. Although, as we have seen, the lobster's normal method of progression is walking along the sea-bed, it can and often does rise into the water and swim backwards with powerful flexing movements of its tail. In the members of the last two decapod sub-orders there is a gradual reduction of the abdomen until in the true crabs it has become little more than a vestige with very limited functions. In this chapter we shall trace the first part of this reduction as it is shown by the members of the sub-order Anomura, the best-known members of which are the hermit crabs.

The least modified members of the sub-order are the squat lobsters. In its general appearance a squat lobster looks like a small edition of an ordinary lobster, but its body, including the abdomen, is more flattened and relatively broader, so that the legs are carried wider apart. The abdomen, too, is relatively shorter and less powerful, though it has a well-developed tail fan. Whereas, however, the lobster

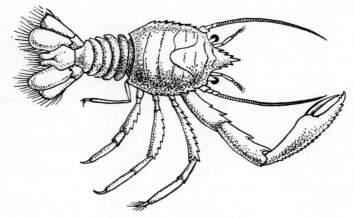

Fig. 38. A typical squat lobster

normally carries its abdomen extended beyond its thorax, the squat lobster's abdomen is almost invariably turned forward and held tightly against the under surface of its thorax. If it is startled it can, however, extend its abdomen and use it to swim backwards through the water. Such movement, though, is exceptional and always of short duration, and cannot be maintained indefinitely as it can in the lobster. The first of the five pairs of thoracic walking-limbs are well developed with powerful claws. The next three pairs form walking-limbs, none of which carry small pincers as do the first two pairs in the lobster. The last pair are much reduced in size, and are normally folded into the gill chamber, being much too weak to play any effective part in supporting the body.

There are five British species of squat lobsters, all of small size. Only the two largest species commonly occur on the shore, though specimens of the other three, which live in the shallow off-shore waters, may occasionally be found on the lower parts of the shore during the spring and early summer. On shore they are most likely to be found in rock pools or under stones not too far from the low-tide mark. The more common of the two shore species is *Galathea squamifera*, which is greenish brown in colour and between two and three inches long. Much more attractive in appearance is the spiny squat lobster, *Galathea strigosa*, whose body is bright red decorated with blue lines and spots. It is about an inch longer than the previous species, and although this does not make it a very big animal, it is noted for its pugnacity. With its flat claws it is able to give quite a good, and at times painful, account of itself if disturbed.

The three offshore species, which may occasionally be found sheltering under stones or seaweed on the lower parts of the shore in the spring, are *Galathea nexa* and *Galathea dispersa*, each about 1½ inches long, and *Galathea intermedia*, which is less than one inch in length. The general colour of *Galathea nexa* is red with blue markings. Unlike any of the other squat lobsters its chelipeds are thickly covered with feathery setae which give them a very furry appearance. *Galathea dispersa* lacks any blue colouring, and its whole surface has a very roughened appearance. *Galathea intermedia* is quite common under stones in rock pools low down the shore, but is not easy to find because it is seldom more than three-quarters of an inch in length.

Although they do not use their abdomens much, the squat lobsters still have them fairly well developed. The reduction of the abdomen is carried a stage further in the so-called porcelain crabs, of which we have two common British shore representatives. If you are searching under stones fairly well down the shore you may well find specimens of our smallest crab, the smooth porcelain crab, *Porcellana longicornis*. Its cephalothorax, which measures only a few millimetres across, is almost circular, and so looks much like that of a true crab. Its abdomen, however, betrays its true affinities. Although reduced as in all the Anomura and the Brachyura or true crabs, and carried normally tucked beneath the carapace, it still retains its tail fan, which is never present in any of the true brachyuran crabs. In the female in addition to the pair of uropods, the appendages of the fifth abdominal segment, there are also four pairs of pleopods representing the appendages of the first four abdominal segments. In the male, however, only the first pair of pleopods have been retained.

The shell of the smooth porcelain crab is whitish in colour, and very smooth. The claws are relatively enormous, being longer than the carapace. The first three pairs of thoracic walking-legs end in sharp spines, but the last pair are much reduced in size and are carried pointing upwards. The antennae are relatively very long and slender.

Somewhat larger but more local in its distribution is the hairy porcelain crab, *Porcellana platycheles*. Its claws are broad and flattened, each being nearly as large as the carapace, and fringed with long setae to which sand and mud particles cling. These, together with the dull reddish brown or greyish colour of the upper surface of the carapace, to which sand and mud particles also cling, serve to camouflage the little crab and make it difficult to detect. The body and claws are both flattened, and the animal clings closely to the under surface of rocks and stones, using the sharply pointed spines at the ends of the three larger pairs of walking-legs to maintain its grip. Thus holding firmly, and offering the minimum of resistance to the water because of its extreme flattening, the hairy porcelain crab is in little danger of being washed away even in a stormy sea.

Another interesting group of anomurans are the so-called burrowing prawns, which are not prawns at all but rather unusual relatives of the squat lobsters and the hermit crabs. They are really creatures of the shallow off-shore waters but they can be found in muddy sand by digging at extreme low water during spring tides. They are all burrowers, and are only found on the south and east coasts. Unlike the other members of the sub-order they normally carry the abdomen stretched out behind the thorax. It is, however, not very powerful, though it is broad and flat, and could not be used for strong swimming like the abdomen of true prawns. *Callianassa subterranea* is about two inches in length, and red in colour, with a flat abdomen almost twice as long as the rest of the body. The two claws, which are the first of the five pairs of thoracic walking-limbs, are extremely unequal in size, one being three or four times the size of the other, and this larger one may belong to either side.

While *Callianassa* merely sinks itself into the sand, the other two species, *Upogebia stellata* and *Upogebia deltaura* construct deep permanent burrows which open at the surface at several points, each burrow containing a pair.

In their methods of feeding the burrowing prawns and the porcelain crabs differ from most other decapods. Instead of procuring fairly large particles of food and breaking these up with their mouth parts, they feed on microscopic organisms which they strain from the water by means of fringes of setae on their mouth parts.

The most fascinating of all the anomurans are the hermit crabs, which are indeed among the most interesting of all the animals of the sea-shore. There are several different species, but in their general habits they are very similar. The hermit crab is an animal with a perpetual housing problem, always needing a new and larger house as it grows. It has lost the protective armour from its abdomen, so for safety it keeps it tucked away in a discarded winkle, whelk or other shell appropriate to its size.

If you examine carefully the shells on the bottom of a rock pool you may well see one suddenly scuttle away on a couple of pairs of legs. If you pick it up to have a look at it you will probably feel a jerk, and may even hear a click, as the legs are suddenly withdrawn into the shell, leaving one claw visible, blocking the entrance to the shell. This is always the right claw, very much larger than the left one which is always tucked in behind it. Like the claws of any crab, it is a useful weapon, but its main function is to act as an armoured door to keep intruders out.

Fig. 39. A hermit crab removed from its borrowed shell to show its structural modifications

Every part of the hermit crab's body is modified to fit in with its unusual existence. Its unprotected abdomen, which has been likened to a cellophane bag filled with pink flesh, is permanently twisted so as to fit easily into the coils of the adopted shell. Only the first two pairs of walking-legs are well developed and used for walking, the other two pairs being much reduced in size and kept permanently within the shell. The abdominal swimmerets, too, have become much reduced to functionless rudiments, except in the female, in which they are still used for attaching the developing eggs, as we shall see later. The last pair of abdominal appendages, the uropods, have become modified to form a pair of sickle-shaped hooks. These are used to anchor the abdomen to the central pillar of the adopted shell, thus making it almost impossible to drag the crab from its shell without injuring it.

The behaviour of the hermit crab within its shell has been observed by persuading it to make its home in a glass model of a shell. Whenever anything moves within its field of vision the grip of the abdominal hooks on the shell is tightened, and further anchorage is given by the two hind pairs of thoracic legs, which are braced so as to hold the body of the crab firmly against the inside of the shell. If danger really threatens it is the sudden contraction of the muscles of the abdomen which serves to withdraw the animal into its shell with a click. These are the same muscles which flex the lobster's tail and enable it to swim rapidly backwards.

The hermit crab begins life like all other crabs as a free-swimming larva which is quite symmetrical, but it soon changes to a tiny hermit crab with an asymmetrical twisted abdomen. Now begins its lifelong house hunt. A very tiny shell suffices at first, but the little creature grows rapidly, and frequent moves become necessary, each time into a slightly larger house.

Removal into a new house is amusing to watch in an aquarium tank. First the new shell is carefully explored with claws and antennae to make sure that it is uninhabited and clean. If it is suitable, the move is accomplished with great rapidity, the abdomen being quickly withdrawn from the original shell and thrust into the new one. The hermit crab certainly behaves as though it realizes the danger of leaving its unprotected abdomen exposed for longer than necessary. So obsessed is it with the passion for house-hunting that even when quite suited for the time being it cannot resist examining every empty shell it comes across. Presented in an aquarium with a number of empty shells of different sizes, it will always examine each one carefully before choosing one for its new home.

With its unprotected abdomen safely tucked away within the coils of the mollusc shell, the hermit crab is an exceedingly pugnacious little creature, always ready to engage in combat with its fellows. Sometimes there is a fierce struggle between two hermits for the possession of a new home. Any crab which has been unwise enough to move into a house which is a little too big for it may well be unable to resist the efforts of an attacker to eject it, but in a house of the right size it is able to anchor itself firmly enough to resist ejection.

Like other decapod Crustacea, the female hermit crab carries her developing eggs attached to her abdominal appendages. Because of the asymmetry of the abdomen only those on the left side are developed sufficiently to be used for this purpose. They are well supplied with setae to which the eggs can be attached. Each female is able to carry several thousand eggs and periodically, when no danger threatens, she will come out of her shell to aerate them by waving them about in the water. When they are ready to hatch she again emerges from the shell and gently brushes off the eggs into the water with the last thoracic appendage on the left side. This, and its fellow on the right side, are well supplied with hairs, and are thought to be used to brush out any

The Hermit Crabs and their Relatives

detritus which may become deposited in the gill chambers.

In contrast to their intolerance towards other members of their own species, hermit crabs enter into partnership with a variety of other animals. Such partnerships between two species for the mutual benefit of both are known as commensalism, and the almost invariable associations between hermit crabs and certain species of sea anemones are among the classic examples of commensalism.

Of the several British species of hermit crabs the one most commonly found in rock pools on the sea-shore is *Eupagurus bernhardus*. This is the largest of our hermits, full-grown specimens attaining a length of up to six inches. In the rock pools, however, only immature specimens are found, and these will be occupying the shells of periwinkles, top shells and dog whelks. At this stage they seldom enter into association with other species. When they become full grown, however, they forsake the sea-shore for the shallow off-shore waters, where they change these smaller shells for those of the whelk. Having now nearly reached full size, there is no longer any need to change house frequently, and this makes it more practical to take in one or more lodgers.

Almost every full-grown specimen will carry an anemone belonging to the species *Calliactus parasitica* firmly fixed to the top of its adopted whelk shell. Both partners undoubtedly gain from this association. Despite the added burden the crab seems to welcome its guests. It does in fact probably derive considerable benefit from the presence of the anemone, which not only helps to camouflage it, but also serves to warn off its enemies, which prefer to remain at a safe distance from the anemone's batteries of sting cells in its tentacles. The anemone benefits by being carried around to various feeding-grounds, when it also shares in the crab's meals. Whenever the crab stops to eat, the anemone bends

right forward until its tentacles sweep the ground in front
of the crab's mouth, and are able to pick up particles of food
which the crab drops.

Besides the anemone on the top of the shell the hermit
crab often has a second guest, one of the ragworms, *Nereis
furcata*, which lives inside the shell alongside the crab's body.
Although the ragworms are equipped with powerful jaws,
their bodies are unarmed, so they are very vulnerable to
their enemies. *Nereis furcata* gains protection when living in
association with the hermit crab, and feeding is also made
easy for it. Whenever the crab has a meal, the worm thrusts
its head out of the shell and shares it. The benefit of this
partnership to the crab is less obvious. It is probable though
that the worm helps to keep the inside of the whelk shell
clean by devouring any particles which become adhered to
it, and it may also help to keep the respiratory current of
water circulating.

Philip Henry Gosse, in his famous book *The Aquarium*,
published in 1856, first described this association between
the hermit crab and the worm. He refers to the hermit as a
soldier crab, a term best not used today since it is now used
for a different group of tropical shore crabs, which we shall
meet in the next chapter. He has been describing the association between the hermit and the anemone, and goes on:
'But I find that this association is not the only one that exists
here. While I was feeding one of my Soldiers, by giving him
a fragment of cooked meat, which he, having seized with
one claw, had transferred to the foot jaws (maxillipeds), and
was munching, I saw protude from between the body of the
Crab and the Whelk-shell the head of a beautiful worm,
Nereis bilineata (now called *furcata*), which rapidly glided out
round the Crab's left cheek, and, passing between the upper
and lower foot-jaws, seized the morsel of food, and, re-

treating, forcibly dragged it from the Crab's very mouth. I beheld this with amazement, admiring that, though the Crab sought to recover his hold, he manifested not the least sign of anger at the actions of the Worm. I had afterwards many opportunities of seeing this scene enacted over again; indeed, on every occasion that I fed the Crab and watched it eating, the Worm appeared after a few moments, aware, probably by the vibrations of its huge fellow-tenant's body, that feeding was going on, and not I think by any sense of smell. The mode and the place of the Worm's appearance were the same in every case, and it invariably glided to the Crab's mouth between the two left-foot jaws. I was surprised to observe what a cavern opened beneath the pointed head of the *Nereis* when it seized the morsel, and with what force comparatively large pieces were torn off and swallowed, and how firmly the throat-jaws held the piece when the latter would not yield. Occasionally it was dragged quite a way from the Crab's jaws, and quickly carried into the recesses of the shell; sometimes in this case he put in one of his claws and recovered his morsel; at others he gave a sudden start at missing his grasp, which frightened the Worm and made it let go and retreat; but sometimes the latter made good his foray, and enjoyed his plunder in secret.'

In addition to these regular commensals, the common hermit crab often has colonies of two sedentary animals growing on the roof of its home. These are the hydroid *Hydractinia echinata*, a colonial coelenterate related to the sea anemones and corals, and the sponge *Ficulina ficus*. Whether these represent partners or are merely un-cooperative squatters is difficult to decide. Of course both will contribute to the crab's camouflage.

Eupagurus bernhardus is found on all British coasts. The

only other hermit crab likely to be found on our shores in any numbers is *Eupagurus prideauxii*. It is a much smaller species than the common hermit, full-grown specimens seldom exceeding 2½ inches in length, and it is more at home in the shallow water beyond the low-tide mark than on the shore. In its general habits it is very similar to the larger species, choosing smaller specimens of whelk shells for its home. It, too, lives in partnership with a sea anemone, but of a different species, *Adamsia palliata*. Instead of fixing its basal disc to the top of the whelk shell like *Calliactus*, it wraps it right round the shell, the margins fusing together where they meet beneath it. Once this has been achieved the anemone is virtually committed to the shell for life, apparently only leaving it if its companion dies. As it grows it covers more and more of the shell. Eventually it grows beyond the mouth of the shell, thus increasing the shell's effective capacity. This means that as the hermit grows it also has no need to seek out another larger home. Eventually it is enclosed partly by the original shell and partly by the tube made by the extended basal disc of the anemone. *Nereis furcata* also occurs in the shell occupied by *Eupagurus prideauxii*, though perhaps less frequently than it does in association with *bernhardus*. *Hydractinia* is also quite commonly found on the shell.

The only other British species of hermit crab of importance is *Eupagurus cuanensis* Except accidentally specimens of this species will never be found on the shore, for it is an exclusively shallow-water species. Its principal partner is the sponge *Ficulina ficus*, already mentioned as a doubtful commensal of *Eupagurus bernhardus*. With *Eupagurus cuanensis*, however, the relationship leaves no room for doubt. Early in its life the hermit chooses a shell which already has a small specimen of the sponge growing on it. As both animals continue to grow the sponge gradually extends beyond the shell until it has grown right round the crab, leaving a sufficient opening through which its head, claws and legs can still emerge. Although the sponge can offer the crab no active protection against attack from its enemies, being completely devoid of weapons of any kind, it is probably of considerable benefit as a camouflage for it. Sponges are little sought after for food, only certain species of sea slugs showing any interest in them, and they could certainly not harm the hermit crab.

Hermit crabs are found almost everywhere in the world. There are some which live in very deep water, and these show a very interesting association with certain colonial sea anemones, large numbers of which cluster together on the same rock surface. These hermit crabs do not live in borrowed shells. Instead they tuck their unprotected abdomens between the anemones, where, of course, they are quite safe from attack. At 2,000 fathoms and more, where these animals live, no sunlight penetrates, so that it is completely dark. Nevertheless the crabs have eyes as well developed as those of their relatives on the shore and in the shallow seas. The anemones among which they live are phosphorescent, and it is thought that the crabs can see to catch their prey as it passes by with the aid of the light which these anemones produce.

More remarkable are the land hermits which exist in great numbers in many tropical countries. These spend the bulk of their lives on land, often several miles inland from the coast, adopting the empty shells of land snails as their homes instead of the shells of sea-shore and marine snails. Like the vertebrate amphibia, however, although they have themselves become emancipated from water, they still have to return to it to breed. Each year therefore at the breeding season they return to the water so that the larvae which hatch from their eggs can be released into the sea. After the usual planktonic life these change to small hermit crabs which can follow their parents out of the water on to the land.

To enable them to breathe out of water these land hermits, which are all species of the genus *Coenobita*, have specially modified respiratory arrangements. The internal lining of the gill chamber, that part of the carapace covering in the sides of the thorax, is very well supplied with blood capillaries and is kept moist, so that it functions as a lung. This is supplemented by the skin of the abdomen, which is also moist and well supplied with surface blood capillaries. The land hermits are omnivorous in their diet, eating both plant and animal food. One species, *Coenobita rugosa*, which lives in Florida, is credited with eating the young of terns and other ground-nesting birds. They are quite frequently found well above the ground climbing in shrubs and small trees.

The most remarkable of all the hermit crabs, however, is the so-called robber or coconut crab, *Birgus latro*, which has the distinction of being the largest land crustacean. It is a widespread and common species of the islands in the Pacific and Indian Oceans. The gradual loss of the abdominal armour and its functional replacement by a borrowed shell must have been a long evolutionary process. *Birgus* has reversed this by giving up the shell and reacquiring its own abdominal protection.

Like all the other land hermits it spawns into the sea, the fertilized eggs passing through a larval life similar to that of an ordinary hermit crab. As soon as the larva changes to a crab it leaves the water. At this stage it has a soft unprotected abdomen like any other hermit crab, and it adopts a

The Hermit Crabs and their Relatives

small snail shell as its home. Before it is a year old, however, it has abandoned the shell and developed a secondary calcareous covering to protect its abdomen. This, however, is a new growth, and does not represent the redevelopment of the original cuticle of the hermit crabs' remote ancestors. Unlike all other hermits, too, its abdomen is no longer twisted, but has become quite symmetrical like that of a normal crab.

For breathing in air its carapace cavity has become considerably modified. A septum divides it into an upper and a lower half. The latter, the true gill chamber, contains the complete set of gills, but these are much reduced in size and are functionless. The inner walls of the upper half, however, are produced into a series of feathery tufts which are very well supplied with blood capillaries. These are kept moist and act like the surface of a terrestrial lung.

The early travellers visiting the islands on which the robber crabs live described them climbing coconut palms in order to break off the coconuts which were said to form the main item in their diet. These habits were credited to the crabs for a long time, simply because each author quoted the earlier ones. It seems however, that the robber crab eats all kinds of nuts and fruits, showing a marked preference for those rich in oil. The coconut would of course fit into this category. Older accounts contained vivid descriptions of them tearing off the husks of the coconuts and then breaking through the nut in the region of the eyes with powerful blows of their claws. In recent years, however, several naturalists have investigated the habits of the robber crabs, and their findings do not substantiate the earlier reports. The occasional individual has been observed to remove a little of the husk, but none has stripped a nut completely, while the majority show no interest whatsoever

134

in the complete nut. Even when provided with husked nuts, none of them proved able to open them. Doubtless they would be able to open one which had been cracked on falling, and such cracked nuts probably do form a part of their diet. As to their tree-climbing habits, they are capable of ascending the trunk of a tree if disturbed, but there is no evidence that they do so for the purpose of gathering food.

The robber crab is quite a large creature weighing up to six pounds and having a shell width of at least six inches. The leg span of the first pair of walking legs may be as much as three feet. In climbing it uses the first three pairs of walking-legs, which are provided with long sharp spikes. Normally it ascends and descends head first, and may often be found resting on a trunk a few feet above the ground.

Robber crabs are good to eat, and in some islands they have been exterminated by too much exploitation. On other islands they are thought to have been seriously reduced in numbers by rats introduced accidentally from calling ships. They are not entirely vegetarian in their feeding habits, but will devour any carrion they come across, including dead members of their own kind. They seem to prefer fat to lean meat.

10 · *The True Crabs*

The true crabs, comprising the last Decapod sub-order, the Brachyura, are a highly successful group showing a variety of different types and habits. In the British fauna there are some forty different species, many of which are common and widespread. Besides the typical crabs like the edible crab and the shore crab, there are spider crabs, swimming crabs, pea crabs, masked crabs and sponge crabs.

The best-known member of the crab tribe, apart from the edible crab on the fishmonger's slab, is the little green shore crab, *Carcinus maenas*. It is, too, one of the most successful of all shore animals, being found in abundance on all coasts and on all types of shore, and from the rock pool high up the shore to the rock crevices near the low-water mark. Like the common periwinkle and the mussel, it is almost a universal shore animal, not confined like most shore animals to a certain zone or to a certain type of shore.

The most important difference between the Anomura and the Brachyura is that the reduction of the abdomen has been carried a stage further in the latter, and the carapace or cephalothorax is relatively broader and more compressed than it is in the majority of the members of the former sub-order. This process has already begun, as we have seen, in the porcelain crabs.

136

The True Crabs

Typical crabs like the shore crab have given up swimming altogether, and they carry their abdomens permanently tucked forward beneath the thorax. If we examine several specimens we shall find that there are two distinct types. In one the reduced abdomen, or apron as it is now called, is very narrow and pointed, and consists of five segments, whereas in the other it is still quite broad, and has seven segments. The former is the male crab and the latter the female, the seventh segment representing the telson. The abdominal limbs, which form the swimmerets in other decapods, are much reduced in number and in structure. In the male only two pairs have been retained, and these have become modified and adapted for transferring the spermatozoa to the female at mating. Four pairs have survived in the female. They are well supplied with setae and are used to attach the eggs at the breeding season. They have thus retained one of the two functions for which the swimmerets are responsible in the females of swimming decapods. In neither sex is a tail fan retained at the end of the abdomen. Because the abdomen is so reduced it is of no use for swimming in any of the Brachyura.

The shore crab is a very active little creature, and if you disturb it in hiding under a stone or beneath a rock ledge it will scuttle away with a curious sideways movement, using all four pairs of walking-legs. It is also a very pugnacious animal, and very quick to attack if it gets half a chance. Although it is only a small animal, seldom exceeding a width of two inches, the muscles working its claws are very powerful, and it is advisable to treat them with respect, for they can give a very painful nip. If you want to pick up a specimen do so by holding firmly on to the hind edge of the carapace, when your fingers will be out of reach of its claws. Experimental measurements on the strenght of the claws of the shore crab have shown that the left claw is capable of supporting a weight equal to about thirty times that of the body weight, and the right claw is usually more powerful than this. For comparison, the grip of a man's right hand is only equivalent to a force equal to about two thirds of his body weight.

A favourite method of hiding is to wriggle into the sand until only the two stalked eyes are showing. In this position the little crab is difficult to see, but if any unsuspecting small animal suitable as food passes too close a claw is shot out to capture it. Like all crabs and many other Crustacea the shore crab is a scavenger, eagerly devouring any dead or decaying animal material it comes across. Most of us have seen small boys fishing for shore crabs from harbour walls or quays, using revolting half-decayed pieces of flesh attached to long pieces of string. The crabs cling to the meat and can be brought up in great quantities, only a sudden jerk persuading them to relinquish their hold on what is to them a desirable meal.

If, instead of holding a crab by its carapace, you pick it up by one of its claws or walking-legs, do not be alarmed if it gives a sudden jerk and runs off leaving the severed limb in your hands. One of the dangers a shore animal has to face is the possibility of getting its limbs trapped beneath a stone rolled by the movement of the water. As a method of escape, crabs and certain other Crustacea are able to shed trapped limbs with little lasting inconvenience to themselves, a phenomenon known as autotomy. These breaks always occur at the third joint of the limb, counting from the body. At this joint there is a special autotomizer muscle, whose contraction serves to break the limb along a special breaking plane. No muscles are severed, and the broken ends of the nerves and blood-vessels are very quickly sealed in a bloodclot.

The True Crabs

At the next moult a miniature new limb makes its appearance, and this gets progressively bigger with each succeeding moult, until eventually the damaged limb becomes as large as and indistinguishable from its undamaged fellow on the other side of the body. This ability to regenerate lost limbs was the basis of a rather cruel practice which prevailed at one time among Spanish fishermen, when crab claws had a high market value. They used to remove the claws from all the crabs they caught and then throw them back into the sea so that in time they might each provide another pair.

Moulting occurs as it does with all Crustacea. The adult shore crab moults once a year, and is a very neat process. A split appears just where the apron and carapace meet, and through the crack so formed the naked crab emerges backwards. The discarded shell is wonderfully complete and really looks like a whole crab, complete with the outer covering of the eyes and the horny layer and teeth which line the crab's stomach. Young crabs grow more quickly than old ones, and for the first year or two there are several moults a year.

Moulting, of course, is necessary for growth in an animal which has an external skeleton, as we have already seen. But with crabs in particular, the moult serves another useful purpose. The back of the crab's carapace offers a particularly suitable site for barnacles and other sedentary organisms, and many crab shells become encrusted with them. They are unable to remove them by their own efforts, but when the old shell is moulted all the previous year's accumulation of uninvited guests is also discarded.

At mating-time the smaller female travels about on the back of her larger mate. Later she may be found with a mass of eggs bulging out from between her apron and carapace, attached to the hairy swimmerets and shielded by the wide apron. Eventually each hatches to a tiny grotesque zoea larva. Before John Vaughan Thompson's work, which we have already referred to in connection with the development of the barnacles, these little creatures were considered to be animals in their own right, members of the permanent plankton, each being called a zoea.

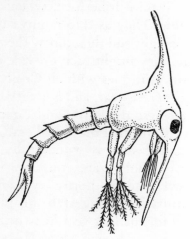

Fig. 40. A typical crab zoea larva

The zoea larva is characterized by a long spine which projects backwards from the middle of the dorsal surface of the thorax, and an equally long rostrum which projects forwards. There is a well-defined abdomen which continues the general line of the body and is not tucked beneath the thorax. As they grow, these zoea larvae undergo several growth moults without any fundamental change of shape. Then finally comes another moult and a completely different megalopa larva results. This, too, was originally regarded as a member of the permanent plankton. Its name refers to its relatively enormous pair of eyes. It does look more like a minute crab, with a broad flat carapace, five pairs of well-

developed thoracic limbs and an abdomen carried outstretched and provided with five pairs of tiny feathery
appendages.

Fig. 41. Zoea larva of the porcelain crab, with its exception-
tionally long rostrum

The edible crab, *Cancer pagurus*, is very similar in general
structure to the shore crab, but it is a considerably larger
species, and belongs to the off-shore waters. Only during
the summer months are you likely to find small specimens
in rock pools or under weed cover near the low-tide mark.
Apart from the size difference it is easily distinguishable
from its smaller relative by the pinkish or reddish brown
colour of its shell, and by its black-tipped claws. Among the
Crustacea the edible crab is one of the most important
species economically. Wherever there are off-shore rocks
there will almost certainly be crabs, and the method of
catching them in pots is the same as that already described
for catching lobsters. The two species live on similar ground,
and are often caught together.

The edible portion of the lobster consists mainly of the
muscles of the abdomen, with the meat of the claws making
a smaller contribution. With the crab, which lacks the
abdominal muscles, the only white meat available is in the
claws and the legs. The rest of the edible material comes
from inside the carapace, the sides of which are occupied by
the crab's exceptionally large liver, which crab lovers regard
as the luxury. Crabs vary very much in condition, and are
best when this liver is firm and bright red. Male crabs are

generally said to have a better flavour than females, provided, of course, that both are equally firm. Edible crabs
grow to a considerable size, some achieving a weight of
12 lb., with a carapace nearly a foot across. Certain areas are
noted for their exceptional crabs, though why some rocks
should habitually produce giant crabs is not known. For
example, the rocks around Cadgwith on the Lizard penin-
sular in Cornwall have the reputation of producing some
of the largest and finest crabs in Britain.

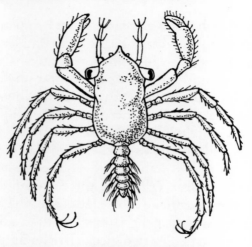

Fig. 42. Typical crab megalopa larva

Similar in general build to the edible crab but much
smaller are the two species of furrowed crabs, so-called
because the upper surface of the carapace has a series of deep
furrows which gives it a rugged appearance. *Xantho incisus* is
reddish brown in colour and has a carapace about three
inches broad. It occurs in Devon and Cornwall and also in
the Hebrides. It is nowhere very common, but the related
Xantho hydrophilus is a rare species which seldom comes on
shore. Its colouring is yellow and red.

For the remainder of this chapter we shall be dealing with Brachyura species which are modified in some way, either structurally or functionally. The sponge crab, *Dromia vulgaris*, is really a Mediterranean species which does sometimes appear on the Cornish coast. It forms a regular commensal partnership with the sponge *Ficulina ficus*, which we have already met in partnership with hermit crabs. The sponge

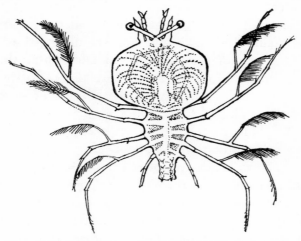

Fig. 43. Phyllosoma larva, which replaces the megalopa larva
in the life history of the crawfish

crab is similar in appearance to the edible crab, but is much smaller, seldom exceeding three inches in carapace width. Its last pair of walking-legs, however, are turned permanently upwards and provided with small pincers, for what purpose we shall see in a moment. When it is quite young the crab searches for a small specimen of the sponge, and when it has found it, carefully places it on the top of its carapace, which is well supplied with setae, giving it a hairy appearance. Here it is held in place by the upturned last pair of legs already mentioned. As the crab grows, so also does the sponge, until it forms a yellow cap fitting right over the carapace and concealing the crab beneath. When at rest with its legs and claws tucked away the crab is quite invisible to any enemy viewing it from above.

The smallest of the British true crabs is the pea crab, *Pinnotheres pisum*, which has become adapted to a semi-parasitic existence. It is pale yellowish or grey, with a rounded carapace. The males grow to a maximum breadth of a quarter of an inch, while the females are somewhat bigger, attaining a maximum breadth of one-third of an inch. For protection they take up residence within the shells of living mussels, oysters or cockles, the majority being found in mussels. They rely for their living upon stealing some of the molluscs' food, and even perhaps occasionally taking a nibble at their gills or mantle. These bivalve molluscs feed on diatoms and other microscopic members of the plankton. A respiratory current of water is drawn into the shell and passes through the perforated curtain-like gills. The suspended plankton organisms are trapped on the gill surface and are then carried forward to the mouth in a current of mucus. The respiratory current and the mucus current are both caused by the rhythmical beating of minute hair-like cilia. The pea crab appropriates some of these trapped organisms for its own use, lying handily placed between the curtains of gills.

Full-grown females sometimes become too large to be able to get out of the mollusc shell, where they are thus confined as prisoners for the remainder of their lives. This is really no hardship to them, except at the breeding season. The difficulty is overcome, however, by the smaller male visiting the female in her prison to mate with her. The fertilized eggs are shed into the mantle cavity of the mollusc, whence they are carried to the exterior in the outgoing respiratory current. It is an interesting fact that pea crabs are generally found only in well-nourished molluscs, seldom being found in those which are not doing so well. The way in which the pea crab behaved within the mollusc shell was investigated by the ingenious device of cutting a window in a mollusc shell which had been adopted by a pea crab.

The female of another tiny crab also finds itself a prisoner in its home when it reaches full size. This is the gall crab, *Hapalocarcinus*, found only in tropical seas, where it forms a partnership with coral. Coral consists of huge colonies of animals looking very much like tiny sea anemones, to which they are in fact closely related. Unlike anemones, however, each one builds a hard cup of limestone around its base. Because the members of the colonies live very close together these cups join up to form great masses of limestone. Each generation of coral animals forms its cups on top of those left by earlier generations, and in this way massive coral reefs are built up.

The young female gall crab chooses for its future home a small space surrounded by young coral animals. As they grow they adjust the shape of their cups so as to form a cavity in which the crab can live in complete safety, making it large enough for the crab when it has eventually grown to full size. A small opening is left through which the imprisoned female crab can draw in a current of water for feeding and respiration. The males live outside the coral, and as they are much smaller than the females they can pass through the openings into the cavities to visit them at the breeding season.

Most groups of animals found on the sea-shore have some members adapted to a burrowing existence in sand, mud or gravel, and the crabs are no exception. Burrowing is of course an admirable way of escaping the attentions of enemies, but it does pose certain problems and necessitates structural modifications to solve them. The burrowing crab, *Corystes cassivelaunus*, has an oval carapace on which there are furrows suggesting the outlines of a face. It is for this reason that the creature is also known as the masked crab. All four pairs of walking-legs are well developed, as are the claws, which are much longer in the male than in the female.

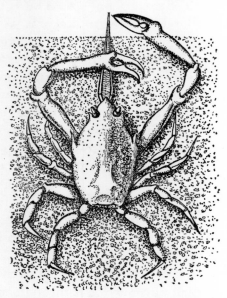

Fig. 44. The burrowing crab, *Corystes cassivelaunus*, lying buried vertically in the sand with only the tips of its antennae projecting above the surface

If a living specimen is placed on the surface of the sand it does not attempt to walk away as any other crab would do, but proceeds to sit up in a vertical position and dig down into the sand with forward and upward sweeping movements of the walking-limbs. Within a very short time it has sunk out of sight, leaving only the tips of its very long antennae projecting above the surface to betray its presence.

These antennae represent the masked crab's most important adaptation, enabling it to live in the sand. Normally a crab draws in a respiratory current of water at the sides of the thorax, passes it over its gills, and then gets rid of it through the front openings of the gill chambers, which lie on either side of the mouth. If the current flowed in the reverse direction, particles of the crab's food might well be drawn in with it, and would thus foul the gills. When the masked crab lies buried, however, it would be impossible for it to maintain this current without drawing in quantities of sand which clog the gill chambers.

Close examination of the masked crab's antennae shows that each is provided with a double row of hairs, and that the two antennae interlock so that the four rows of hairs form a tube. When the crab lies buried in the sand the tip of this tube projects just above the surface clear of the sand, and down it a current of clean water is drawn. This enters the front openings of the gill chambers, and leaves at the sides, thus reversing the normal direction of the respiratory current. This does not matter, because so long as the crab lies buried it does not feed. The hairs are set sufficiently close together to prevent sand grains getting into the tube to block it up. *Corystes* is thought to lie buried during the daytime to avoid the fish which would otherwise eat it. At night, however, it comes out of hiding to forage for food, and it is interesting that as soon as it comes up to the surface it reverses the direction of its respiratory current, entering at the side of the carapace and travelling up the antennal tube.

From the point of view of adaptation none of our crabs are more interesting than the swimming crabs. In the previous chapters we have traced the gradual change from decapods which are primarily swimmers to those which have completely lost the ability to swim through a progressive reduction of the abdomen, the chief organ of propulsion in the swimmers. In the swimming crabs we have an excellent example of the way in which an ancestral ability can be reacquired through an entirely different means. Instead of redeveloping a swimming tail worked by powerful abdominal muscles they have modified their last pair of thoracic limbs for swimming. The last segment of each of these has become flattened to form a horizontal paddle, and both limbs are turned upwards so that the paddles lie on a level with the top of the carapace. In swimming these paddles are moved rapidly up and down in the water, driving the crab forward at a considerable speed. From a supposed likeness of this to the movement of a fiddler playing his violin, the swimming crabs are also known as fiddler crabs, a name which is also used for quite a different group of tropical crabs. On shore swimming crabs are most likely to be found when the tide is out lurking among the weeds covering the rocks near the low-tide mark. If one is found it should be treated with respect, for swimming crabs are among the most vigorous and pugnacious of all the crabs.

Upward of a dozen different species of swimming crabs have been recorded from British waters, but only three of these are likely to be found on the shore. The largest and fiercest of them is the velvet swimming crab, *Portunus puber*, a handsome species some four inches in breadth. Its shell is covered with a reddish brown velvety pile of close-set setae, which accounts for its name, and its legs have blue joints and are decorated with longitudinal black lines. When disturbed, the velvet swimming crab will often dance about and crash its claws together above its carapace as though it is in a rage. To the French fishermen this species has always been known as *le crabe enragé*.

The True Crabs

Gosse managed to keep a velvet swimming crab in an aquarium tank for some time and was able to confirm its pugnacious reputation, which did not stop short even with relatives. 'Our giant crab had no respect for lesser crabs, except a taste for their flesh. I had two or three full-grown soldier crabs (*Eupagurus bernhardus*); themselves warriors of no mean prowess; two, at least, of these fell a prey to the fierce fiddler. His manner of proceeding was regular and methodical. Grasping the unthinking soldier by the thorax, and crushing it so as to paralyse the creature, he dragged the body out of the protecting shell. The soft, plump abdomen was the bonne-bouche; this was torn off and eaten with gusto, while the rest of the animal was wrenched limb from limb with savage wantonness, and the fragments scattered in front of his cave.'

The other two species of swimming crabs likely to be found on the shore are the cleanser or wrinkled crab, *Portunus depurator*, and the marbled swimming crab, *Portunus marmoreus*. Neither of these has hairs on the carapace, and each is only about half the size of the velvet swimming crab. All three species are most likely to turn up on the south and west coasts.

Our swimming crabs are but poorly adapted for swimming compared with related swimming crabs which are widely distributed in tropical and subtropical waters. In these more skilful swimmers all four pairs of walking-legs are adapted for swimming in varying degrees. 'None of our native crabs', wrote Gosse, 'are at the top of the tree in the swimming profession; their efforts, even those of the best of them, are awkward bunglings, when compared with the freedom and fleetness of those I have seen in the Caribbean Sea, and among the Gulf weed, in the tropical Atlantic, which shoot through the water almost like a fish, with the feet on the side that happens to be the front all tucked close up, and those on the opposite side stretched away behind, so as to "hold no water", as a seaman would say, and thus offer no impediment to the way. Our species are obliged to keep their pair of sculls continuously working while they swim; a series of laborious efforts just sufficient to counteract the force of gravity; and the sea-saw motion of the bent and flattened joints of the oar-feet is so much like that of a fiddler's elbow, as to have given rise to a very widely adopted appellation of these Crabs, among our marine populace.' These swift crabs are able to chase and catch the fish on which they feed. One such species, called Henslow's swimming crab (*Polybius henslowii*) or the pearly swimming crab, does live in the seas to the south-west of the British Isles, where it comes to the surface to attack mackerel and pollock. Specimens are sometimes washed up on the beaches of Devon and Cornwall. Many of the larger species are edible, and take the place of our edible crab commercially. On the Atlantic coast of North America, for example, the blue crab (*Callinectes sapidus*) is marketed in considerable numbers.

If the swimming crabs are interesting on account of their structural modifications for an unusual mode of life, the spider crabs are no less interesting on account of their habits. There are several common British species. Essentially they are off-shore animals, but they can often be found hiding among the weeds and rocks on the lower parts of the shore. They are easily distinguished from all other crabs by their very long thin legs and relatively small bodies, which are usually more or less triangular in shape. In the majority of species the body is seldom much more than an inch in length, though the leg span may be six inches or more. The front of the shell is continued forward as a beak or rostrum, from the sides of which the eye-stalks project. Despite their long legs, spider crabs are very slow and awkward in their movements, giving the impression that every movement is painful.

Although they are quite common, these spider crabs are not easy to find, for their shells are generally covered with seaweeds and all kinds of sedentary animals growing on them. As mentioned earlier in the chapter, certain sedentary animals, such as acorn barnacles, often make their homes on a crab's back, and whether the crab likes it or not, it has no means of dislodging them except when it moults. The curious thing about the excessive animal and plant growth on the spider crab's back is that, far from being unwelcome, it is actually planted there by the crab for camouflage. The shell is specially provided with hooked hairs to make attachment easy.

Spider crabs show considerable ability in dressing up, always attaching plants and animals which blend with their surroundings, so as to make them as inconspicuous as possible. If one moves into different surroundings, the old camouflage is removed and a new set planted. Once when a specimen wearing various green seaweeds was put into an aquarium tank where the weeds were all red, it spent many hours laboriously removing the green weeds one by one and replacing them with red ones. To enable a spider crab to do this dressing-up its claws are able to reach every part of its carapace, in contrast to other crabs, and this is a point worth remembering when you handle a spider crab.

The largest of our British spider crabs is the thornback (*Maia squinado*). Its carapace, covered with short spines, measures up to six inches across, and the leg span may be up to two feet. This crab is good to eat, and is caught in considerable numbers in the Channel Islands and on the Continent. On stony beaches the thornbacks bury themselves when the tide goes out until they are just covered, and in earlier times fishermen made use of this habit to locate and catch them. They would walk along the beach when the tide was out in their bare feet, locating the crabs as their spines penetrated their soles!

The most common British shore species are *Hyas araneus*, *Hyas coarctatus*, *Inachus dorynchus* and *Inachus dorsettensis*, the last two having relatively longer and thinner legs than the

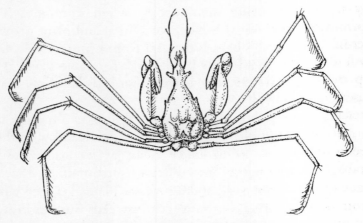

Fig. 45. The beaked spider crab, *Macropodia longirostris*, the most slender of all our spider crabs

first two. The most remarkable British species, however, is the beaked spider crab (*Macropodia longirostris*), which at first glance is very reminiscent of a giant crane-fly. Its legs are several inches long, but incredibly thin. Its reddish body, too, is very slender.

To the spider crabs belongs the distinction of possessing not only the largest crab but the largest crustacean in the world. This is *Macrochira kempferi*, which lives in Japanese waters, where it is caught for food. The outstretched claw span of a full-grown specimen exceeds ten feet, and the claws themselves may be as much as six feet in length.

The partnership between hermit crabs and anemones for their mutual benefit has already been described in the previous chapter. There is one tropical brachyuran crab, *Melia tessalata*, which uses anemones for its own defence even more positively. Since it does not live in a borrowed shell on which it could deposit them, it carries them about, usually holding one in each claw. If the crab is approached by a potential enemy the anemones are held so that their formidable rings of tentacles bar its way. If the crab comes across a larger specimen than one of those it is carrying it will sometimes deposit the smaller one on the rock and take up the larger one to replace it, detaching it carefully by inserting a claw between it and the rock to which it is attached.

Another tropical anemone, *Antholoba rondelettii*, itself seems to play the leading part in its association with various crabs. Normally it lives with its basal disc fixed firmly to the back of the carapace. If for any reason it becomes displaced from its own crab, it lies in wait on the sea-bed in an upside down position. Sooner or later the legs of a crab will come into contact with it, when it immediately attaches itself, folding its basal disc about the limb to avoid being dislodged. From this position it is able at leisure to climb on to the back of the crab and establish itself. It is an interesting point that the anemone, although regarded as one of the more primitive of the invertebrates, is nevertheless apparently able to recognize a crab when it comes in contact with one, for it never seems to be found attached to any other kind of animal.

In tropical countries sandy shores often carry enormous populations of burrowing crabs, which come up to the surface to feed only as the tide recedes, being safely hidden away again in their burrows before the water returns. These crabs are of two main kinds, called soldier crabs and calling crabs, but their habits are somewhat similar. The soldier crabs are lightly built with small round bodies and long thin legs reminiscent of those of our spider crabs, though they are not related. As the tide goes out these little crabs heave themselves out of the sand in their thousands, and their first preoccupation is with feeding. In this they are unusual. They are not equipped to take substantial pieces of food and deal with them, nor, since they do not feed in water, are they filter feeders. What they in fact do is to scrape up the surface sand and as it were apply it to their faces. In this position they are able to lick from the sand grains the bodies of plankton animals which settled on them as the water receded. As these cleaned grains are pushed upwards past the mouth they accumulate as a small round pellet at the front of the carapace. When it reaches a certain size each pellet is brushed away with one of the claws to make room for the next one. The claws are specially flattened to act as spoons in picking up the sand grains. Feeding is mostly done at the water's edge, the little crabs following the receding tide, being joined all the time by their fellows which burrowed lower down the shore than themselves.

Having at last satisfied their appetites, their behaviour changes. They move a little back from the water's edge to where the sand has already drained and become firm. Here they dig open burrows, throwing out the sand in pellets which are much bigger than the feeding pellets. By this time a well-populated shore may be strewn with pellets of both kinds. Each now having its temporary retreat, these lively little crabs are ready to indulge in their curious social life. As they run around encounters are inevitable. Two adult males if they meet indulge in a kind of ceremonial wrestling contest with their claws. Unlike many crabs, they are incapable of harming each other with these, for they are slender and without much strength. Nevertheless honour seems to be served in some way, because after a short time one of the crabs disengages from the battle and the other indulges in an amusing kind of war dance, jumping up and down and beating the sand with his claws. If a mature male meets a young male or a female, the etiquette is quite different. He picks up the weaker individual and carries it to his temporary burrow. At the entrance he generally releases it and seems to be submitting it to close scrutiny, after which it is allowed to scuttle back to its own burrow. Occasionally, however, a female will be carried right into the burrow. Presumably then mating occurs.

These open burrows are quite different from those which are constructed before the tide comes in, and in which the little crabs will remain until they are once more uncovered at the next tide. Some time before the water is due to reach them they all make their way back to their own chosen part of the shore. Here they proceed to hollow out a depression, depositing the sand they remove around the rim, so that the whole structure looks something like the crater of a volcano. The depression is now deepened, and the sand pellets are carefully added to the original rim until a complete roof is formed. At first this is quite thin, but further excavation serves to add sand to it until it is several inches thick, the burrow now representing a large bubble of air well below the surface, which will provide the crab with sufficient air until it can once again emerge on the surface. Although these crabs are confined to the shore, their gills are adapted for breathing in air rather than in water. They will not in fact intentionally submerge themselves in water.

The True Crabs

Quite closely related to these soldier crabs, and similar to them in their general habits, are the fiddler or calling crabs. These are also numerous and widespread on sandy tropical shores. Their most curious characteristic is that one of the claws of every male is enormously enlarged and highly coloured, usually bright red. It may be larger than the whole of the rest of the body. They are used for a type of formal combat between males similar to that already described as taking place between adult male soldier crabs, but their principal use is much more intriguing. They are used to make various gestures, being either waved up and down, or used to perform a more complicated movement which has been likened to the movement of a bowler's arm, or to an elaborate beckoning. In fact these movements seem to be primarily connected with courtship, and although the females often seem to take little or no notice of the signs, it does sometimes happen that a female appears to respond, and follows the male into his burrow.

These calling crabs feed in just the same way as the soldier crabs, scraping off deposited plankton from surface sand grains just after the tide has gone out. In this activity the adult males are somewhat handicapped, because only the small claw is flattened and adapted for picking up sand. Both kinds, although still confined to the shore, are not dependent upon immersion in water, so that they represent a stage in the evolution of the real land crabs.

The land hermit crabs were dealt with in the previous chapter. They are paralleled by a similar group of true crabs equally well adapted to life on land. The two groups have, of course, been evolved quite independently of one another. These brachyuran land crabs all belong to the family *Gecarcinidae*, and are widespread throughout the tropical and sub-tropical parts of the world, being particularly common in the East and West Indies and near the coasts of West Africa. They are very active creatures which may live several miles from the nearest beach, often being found right up in the coastal hills. Like the shore crabs we have just been considering they are essentially burrowers, each living through the day in the burrow which it has excavated for itself, only coming out to feed at night.

There are probably two good reasons for their nocturnal habits. During the day they would be very vulnerable to all kinds of enemies which shore crabs will not generally expect to encounter. Also, like the land hermits, they rely for their respiration upon a specially developed carapace lining which is well supplied with surface blood capillaries and which therefore must be kept moist to function as a lung. Exposure during the day-time would greatly increase the dangers of desiccation of this surface.

Although they are themselves quite independent of the sea for living, they do have to return to it once a year for reproduction. At this time enormous numbers have been seen making for the coast. Once there the females shed their fertilized eggs into the water, where they are then left to develop unprotected. After a few days the trek back to the country begins.

The land crabs' feeding habits are those of the majority of crabs, for they will eat almost any vegetable or animal material that comes their way, so that they are typical crustacean scavengers. Gosse, in *The Aquarium*, had some rather macabre but accurate observations to make about the scavenging habits of crabs, particularly land crabs, and these will, I think, make a fitting end to our survey of the Malacostraca.

'The crabs are the scavengers of the sea; like the wolves and hyaenas of the land, they devour indiscriminately dead and living prey. The bodies of all sorts of dead creatures are removed by the obscene appetite of these greedy Crustacea; and there is no doubt that many an enormous Crab, whose sapidity elicits praise at the epicure's table, has rioted on the decaying body of some unfortunate mariner. But what of that? Let us imitate the philosophy of the negro mentioned by Captain Crow. On the Guinea Coast people are buried beneath their own huts, and the Land-crabs are seen crawling in and out of the holes in the floor with revolting familiarity: notwithstanding which, they are caught and eaten with avidity. A negro, with whom the worthy Captain remonstrated on the subject, seemed to think this but a reasonable and just retaliation, a sort of payment in kind; replying with a grin and chuckle of triumph: "Crab eat black man; black man eat *he*!"'

Glossary

ANTENNAE—a pair of sensory appendages developed on the fourth head segment.

ANTENNULES—a pair of sensory appendages developed from the second head segment.

APRON—the reduced abdomen of true crabs, carried tucked beneath the thorax.

BIRAMOUS—the two-branched condition typical of all crustacean appendages except the antennules.

BROOD POUCH—a pouch in which fertilized eggs can develop. It may occur on the thorax or on the abdomen.

CARAPACE—a fold of chitin beginning at the back of the head and enclosing part or all of the thorax, and sometimes much of the abdomen as well.

CHELIPEDS—first pair of thoracic walking limbs in decapod Crustacea when provided with pincers or chelae.

CHROMATOPHORE—cell containing pigment, used to vary the colour of its possessor for camouflage purposes.

ECDYSIS—moulting of an external skeleton in order to grow.

ENDITES—additional processes developed along the inner edges of phyllopodia.

ENDOPODITE—the inner branch of a biramous appendage.

Glossary

EPIPODITE—additional process attached to the outer side of a protopodite, often acting as a gill.

EXOPODITE—the outer branch of a biramous appendage.

HERMAPHRODITE—condition in which each individual has a complete functional set of both male and female reproductive organs. Usually cross-fertilization occurs, self-fertilization being rare.

MANDIBLES—a pair of appendages developed on the fourth head segment. These are the first of the jaws or mouth parts, used for manipulating the food.

MAXILLAE, or SECOND MAXILLAE—the third pair of mouth parts, developed on the sixth and last head segment.

MAXILLIPEDS—in the higher Crustacea the appendages of the first three thoracic segments.

MAXILLULES or FIRST MAXILLAE—the second pair of mouth parts, developed on the fifth head segment.

OOSTEGITES—special plates developed on thoracic appendages to form a brood pouch in which fertilized eggs can develop.

PARTHENOGENESIS—the development of eggs without fertilization.

PHYLLOPODIUM—broad-lobed limb with thin skeleton, and lacking the definite joints typical of the stenopodium.

PLEOPOD—flattened paddle-shaped biramous abdominal appendages of the higher Crustacea, used for swimming, and also called swimmerets. They occur on the first five abdominal segments.

PROTOPODITE—the basal portion of each appendage, before it divides into its two branches.

ROSTRUM—forward continuation of the dorsal skeleton of the head. It is usually pointed and often serrated.

SPERMATOPHORE—sac containing spermatozoa, in which they are transferred to the female. In due course she can use them to fertilize her eggs as they are produced and laid.

STATOCYST—balancing organ consisting of a pit lined with tactile bristles and containing a sand grain whose movements are recorded by the nerve fibres attached to these bristles.

STENOPODIUM—typical many-jointed appendage, with a well-developed rigid skeleton.

SWIMMERETS—flattened pleopods of the first five abdominal segments of the higher Crustacea. They are used for slow forward swimming.

TELSON—hind end of the abdomen, often developed as a pair of flattened processes which, together with the uropods, form the tail fan.

UROPODS—flattened appendages of the sixth and last abdominal segment. With the telson they form the tail fan, used for rapid backward movement through the water.

Index

Index

Index

165

Index

Index